NATURE TRAILS

TRAILS

AND ANIMAL TALES

Eileen E. Lantry

REVIEW AND HERALD® PUBLISHING ASSOCIATION
HAGERSTOWN, MD 21740

The author assumes full responsibility for the accuracy of all facts and quotations as cited in this book.

Texts credited to NIV are from the *Holy Bible, New International Version*. Copyright © 1973, 1978, 1984, International Bible Society. Used by permission of Zondervan Bible Publishers.

The author found the following books especially helpful: *The Pacific Crest Trail,* vol. 2, by Jeffrey P. Shaffer and Bev and Fred Hartline (Wilderness Press, 1979) and *The Pacific Crest Trail* by William R. Gray (National Geographic Society, 1975).

This book was
Edited by Richard W. Coffen
Designed by De Laine E. Mayden
Cover and inside illustrations by Jim Paxton
Typeset: 11/14 Universe 45 Light

PRINTED IN U.S.A.

00 99 98 97 96   5 4 3 2 1

R&H Cataloging Service
Lantry, Eileen E.
    Nature trails and animal tales.

        1. Animals—Stories.   I. Title.

                508.79

ISBN 0-8280-0866-3

Dedication

To my grandnephew,

Kenneth Gould,

who hiked the

Pacific Crest Trail in 1993.

Contents

Contents

1

Surprises Around Each Bend

Kenny looked at his dad with a big grin. "I think we're ready to start our final packing," he said, pointing toward a stack of equipment piled on the table and heaped up on the floor. "I can hardly believe school's finally out and we're almost ready to go! What's even better is that God sent someone who can cover for you at the office so that you can get away for several months."

"You're right, Kenny. It's a rare doctor who can leave a busy practice in experienced hands just to enjoy hiking with his son."

Dad returned Kenny's smile with a bigger one. He and his 11-year-old son had spent all winter and most of the spring studying maps, buying backpacking equipment, and making plans. Now with Kenny just out of fifth grade and the whole summer ahead of him, they were ready to begin the longest hike in the United States—all the way from Mexico to Canada. It's called the Pacific Crest Trail.

No, they wouldn't hike the whole 2,600 miles in one trip. That's for hikers who have six months and can travel from 14 to 20 miles a day without stopping. Even then, winter snows may cover the trail, or hikers may find themselves hunkered down in their tents, waiting out a blizzard or two. Progress slows down in bad weather, especially when the trail takes them over lots of snow-covered ground. Even at its best, it's not a trail for sissies!

"We'll rest on the Sabbath, and whenever we see something interesting, we'll take time to stop and watch the animals and birds in the mountains, woods, and deserts. Some hikers push it so hard they miss the beauties along the trail." Dad picked up his camera. "I plan to get some good pictures, even if it does take us several summers to complete the trail."

Kenny, tall for his age, pushed his fingers through his unruly brown hair. "I think I'm in good condition, because I've been hiking over the hills around home every day. Even so, I'm glad we're planning to conquer the Crest Trail a little at a time."

"Me, too. The trail guide suggests we take it by segments between supply points. One of the cautions from the guide book is 'Carry a light pack.' The only way that's possible is never to carry more than an eight day supply of food."

"So how do we eat for the months we'll be on the trail?"

"Takes a lot of planning before we start. Though they're more expensive, freeze-dried food can cut down our pack's weight as much as 15 pounds."

Just then Mother and 6-year-old Heather walked into the room. "How are you ever going to get all that into two backpacks?" Mother shook her head in dismay.

"We're not. We plan to spend the next few evenings making up food packages that you'll mail along the way." Dad smiled at Mother. "You're a vital part of the success of this adventure. I have a list of post offices along or near the trail route. We'll mail the first packages right away, as we need to allow 24 days before we expect to pick them up."

"How do I address the packages? I'd be glad to help right now."

"Thanks, Mom. You're great!" Kenny hugged her. "Here's the information. Address it to Dad and me, General Delivery, the Post Office, state and zip, and mark it 'Hold until a specific date.' Dad's figured out the approximate time it will take us between segments."

"You've always been a master at details and organization. No need to worry about Kenny when you're in charge." Mother's blue eyes twinkled as she cast a loving look at Dad.

"You'll also need to pay for the postal service called Special Handling and phone the post offices to be sure they'll hold our mail until we arrive. You know, legally they're required to hold mail only 10 days. I'll keep a duplicate list of supply places in my backpack, so we'll count on you to keep us full and happy. You can be sure we'll be eager for each package." Dad smiled at her again and added, "See, you'll be taking care of us on the trail, like you always do at home."

"Sure wish we could go, too," Heather said. "How will you find the way and not get lost?"

"Easy. The National Park service has placed trail markers along the way. We'll keep our eyes open for the small triangular shields with a picture of a pine tree against snow-capped mountains." Kenny's blue eyes opened wide as he imagined he'd spotted one nailed to a tree. "And if we're above timberline where there are no trees, we'll look for 'ducks.' They're piles of rocks that have a leaning post with a plastic streamer tied to it pointing the direction to go."

"And we'll follow them into 23 national forests, 14 wilderness areas, and seven national parks," Dad announced. "We'll be hiking the crest of both the Sierra

9

Nevada and Cascade mountain ranges. That's why it's called the Crest Trail."

"Won't you be going near such famous peaks as Mt. Whitney, Mt. Shasta, Mt. Hood, and Mt. Rainier?" Mother asked.

"Right. We'll get to enjoy the most magnificent scenery in the West. But now we'd better get busy organizing all this camping gear."

"I'm sure glad for this lightweight sleeping bag and foam pad. In my practice hikes, I've been wearing my backpack. It's not only comfortable but has lots of pockets where I've put special items." Pocket by pocket he showed them. "See, here's my Bible, a pencil, and notepad. This one has my flashlight, matches, toilet paper, and sunglasses. Here's my toothbrush and toothpaste, first-aid kit, and moleskin for blisters. This one has soap and plenty of insect repellent. I've included several large plastic bags. They'll keep my clothes dry, even if our packs get wet should we get caught in the rain. My clothes and food go in the center part. I'll tie this folding camp shovel on my pack. It'll have many uses but especially for covering our outdoor toilet needs. The trail rules are to bury it far from the trail or any source of water."

"You've prepared well, son. What about your most important piece of clothing, your boots?" Mom asked.

"They're well broken in and really comfortable. See, I also have some Snoseal treatment to keep them waterproof and prevent cracking from heat." Kenny held them up for inspection.

"I didn't see a comb," Heather interrupted. "But you seldom comb your hair at home, so why should you do it on the trail?"

Kenny pushed his fingers through his sandy brown hair, so like his father's. "Why comb it? Just gets messed up again."

"I have a comb to loan to Kenny when I think he needs it. Now it's my turn," Dad said. "I'm taking snowshoes, an ice ax, and two ropes. One rope is to keep our food out of reach of bears. The longer rope will help us over snow-covered parts of the trail or difficult fords when the streams are running high because of snowmelt. I'll carry a two-person tent, a stove, cooking utensils, and some of the food. Kenny's pack will weigh about 25 pounds, but mine will be more than 50 pounds." Dad gave Kenny a friendly poke and added, "You're getting off easy, pal."

Mom helped them pack the food parcels for each trail segment. They spent several evenings studying the map again and choosing post offices where they could pick the food up along or near the route. Even with everything they had to do, it seemed to Kenny that the days would never pass. But finally they were ready to go.

Mom and Heather drove them to the southern part of California near the little town of Campo. Grandpa and Grandma, who live in nearby Arizona, came to join them in the happy send-off. In the early morning shadows of an April sunrise, Dad and Kenny unloaded their hiking gear. Mother looked out over the low hills blanketed by chaparral. "Smell the fragrant sage," she said. But Kenny had spotted the small shield nailed to a fence post. "Here it is! The beginning of the Pacific Crest Trail!" he shouted.

"Come and see what it says on the monument." Heather pointed to it. "See, it tells how far you're going to have to hike."

"But he only has to take it one step at a time," Grandma added.

Dad, looking across the barbed wire fence said, "That separates Mexico from California."

"Don't forget your water canteens. Looks pretty dry out there in the desert." Grandpa added them to the pile. When everything was ready, they all joined hands and bowed their heads while Grandma asked Jesus to keep them safe and close to Him. Kenny felt a lump in his throat as he waved until the car with Mom and Heather disappeared.

Every morning before they started hiking, Dad and Kenny asked God to help them keep their eyes open for the surprises that would pop up everywhere.

2

Did It Rain Toads?

One week had gone by. Both Dad and Kenny discovered that they weren't in top condition. Hiking with a heavy pack was slow going, demanding frequent rest stops. "So far we're covering from 10 to 12 miles a day," Dad announced.

Kenny realized that the desert—hot, dry, and dusty—is alive with mystery and wonder. Several times they spotted a fast hiker ahead of them—the roadrunner. But this large, long-legged bird didn't pay any attention to them. Instead he just raced faster and faster, this way and that, hunting for adventure and food. The hot sun and sand didn't slow the roadrunner in the least. Kenny squatted down to get a closer look at its tracks in the sand—two toes forward, two backward.

During the second week, they hiked in the Anza-Borrego Desert. Dad had to fill his three gallon water bag, plus what Kenny carried in the canteens.

After Dad had dropped iodine purification tablets into the water, he lifted the bag. "Water's not only precious, but might heavy," he groaned.

But the cool, beautiful nights brought a feeling of peace. In the clear, desert air they marveled at the stars, which shone with a brilliance they'd never seen at home. They traced outlines of constellations, followed the streaks of meteors, and let their imaginations wander at the thrill when someday Jesus would take them through the galaxies.

The next day when they sat on a big rock to rest Dad announced, "Kenny, before we get into the mountains and snow, I think we need to know how to use the compass and interpret the maps in the guidebook."

"Why's that so important, Dad?"

"Your navigation skills could determine the difference between life and death. If we got caught in a whiteout, when there's no way to know directions, the compass and the map could help us find our way, even if the trail is buried under the snow. Should you ever be alone in the wilderness, you need these skills."

Kenny got out his compass. "OK, Dad, you convinced me; I'm ready."

"As you know, the most important part of a compass is the magnetized needle that swings until it points north. However, it's not pointing to the true north pole but to the magnetic north pole, which is located near Hudson Bay in Canada."

"Does that make any difference?"

"Indeed it does. Your compass isn't pointing to true north. You must make a correction to allow for the difference. This variation, or declination as it is called, is the number of degrees that the compass needle points east or west of true north. In the United States at Lake Michigan the compass points to true north. Here's a simple rule to help you compensate for declination: Add west; subtract east." Dad opened the PCT guidebook. "See, here it tells you where to set your compass as you begin hiking each section of the trail."

Kenny read, "Declination—20 degrees east."

"Now let's practice using the compass. Here's a map of the trail. Let's pretend that five feet of snow have covered the trail. Since we can't follow it, we must find the next point on the map where we want to go. First we locate the place on the map where we are now, and then we find the point toward which we want to hike. Now lay the plastic base of the compass on the map so that it touches both points."

Kenny did as Dad said. "Step two is to turn the compass housing (the round part that moves on which the degrees are printed) until the printed arrow alines with the north-south lines on the map. Take a look at the degrees marked on the outside of the compass housing. What's the degree beside the direction-of-travel arrow on the plastic base?"

"Let's see. It says 64 degrees."

"Be sure you correct for the east declination by subtracting 20 degrees. You were on 64 degrees. Now turn the housing so that the direction-of-travel arrow on the base plate is opposite 44 degrees. The corrected heading gives you the true direction."

"OK. I've done it. Now what's step three?"

"Turn the entire compass and plastic plate horizontally until the magnetic needle points in exactly the same direction as the printed arrow inside the compass dial. To travel your desired course, follow the direction-of-travel arrow on the base plate. Sight along this arrow to a tall tree or other landmark and go to it. When you reach it, get out your compass and sight again."

"Sounds easy and fun. When I get these three basic steps mastered, I should be able to travel safely cross country wherever I please and find my way back, too. I'm going to practice using my compass often till I feel confident that I know how."

"Sounds good to me! While we're talking about maps, let me point out other helpful things found in our *PCT Guidebook.*"

Dad turned the page. "This mileage table helps hikers know the miles between each point in the section they are hiking. The miles are listed for each direction you're hiking, north to south, or south to north, like we're going. Also listed are supply points and post offices where we can pick up our 'care' packages that Mother is sending us."

Kenny studied the mileage table, figuring out how far they'd hiked. "This will help us make plans for our destination each day. Gives us a goal."

"You'll find this next bit of information most helpful. The authors list the problems we're likely to meet. Maybe it's early season snow patches, mosquitoes, and other insects, or extensive waterless stretches where we'll have to carry more water."

"I'd sure hate to run out of water. Hard hiking really makes me thirsty."

"Let's take a few minutes to look at these topographical maps. They're like a picture of the ground seen from above. Notice the entire map is divided into one-mile boxes called grid patterns."

"What's that mean?"

"One inch on the map equals one mile on the ground."

"Why all those wavy lines?"

"They're called contour lines. They show the elevation above sea level. The closer the lines are to each other, the steeper the mountain or valley. These lines tell you if hiking is on level ground, gently sloping, or so steep that hiking might be very difficult or impossible. The guide also gives a description of what you'll see on each section of the trail.

16

You'll notice a pair of numbers like this—5520-2.8. That means the elevation is 5,520 feet and at a distance of 2.8 miles from your last given point. This description of the route gives us an idea of what to expect as we hike."

"Wow! I've got a lot to learn. I can see I'll spend plenty of time studying the maps and guidebook each day. Sure great that someone before us has prepared all this. Should make our hiking more interesting and save us from making too many mistakes."

"Right, Kenny. Reminds me of the great Guidebook that Jesus gave us. Life will be much more fun if we take time to study God's Guidebook." Dad put the *PCT Guide* back into his pack and added, "I'll help you master the details as we go along. To be good hikers we need to prepare for what's ahead. Now it's time to hit the trail."

That evening when they were still hiking in the desert, Kenny and his dad saw dark clouds rolling across the usually bright blue sky. "It doesn't usually rain this time of the year in the desert," Dad said, "but tonight we'd better pitch our tent instead of sleeping out in the open. Let's find some high ground, and we'd better dig a trench around the tent so that the water will run away from the tent and not under us. I don't like sleeping in a puddle of water. Those clouds look like they mean business."

That night the ping-ping and thud-thud of heavy rain on their tent woke up Kenny and his dad. Then just before dawn, more strange sounds awakened them. What was happening? It sounded almost like barks coming from all directions. "What's out there?" Kenny whispered.

Dad grabbed his flashlight and shone its beam into the darkness. "Well, of all things!" he exclaimed. "Looks like it rained toads last night too. Those guys really make a racket!"

When they crawled out of their tent, Kenny and his dad tried to avoid stepping on the dozens of nearby toads hopping toward the puddles left by the rain.

Once they were on the trail again, Kenny stooped down to look at the jelly-like strings of black dots filling most of the puddles. "I'm sure the toads left these eggs," he muttered to himself, "but where are they now?"

When Spadey the Toad Sings

When the hot sun beats upon the dry earth and temperatures soar to more than 100 degrees, a few desert animals, like lizards, lie in the sun as they wait to catch insects. But not Spadey. The only way he can live in the dry desert is to avoid the heat. He's a great digger and spends most of his life underground.

What does Spadey do during those eight or nine months in the sand? Not much. He stays quiet in his cool burrow, sleeping most of the time. Sometimes he wiggles his four legs and begins to dig upward. He has a super digging tool on his hind feet, a large, horny, spade-like wart. His brown body blends perfectly with the dirt. He's different from other toads because his eyes are vertical or up and down.

Spadey has no idea how long he's slept, but a strange new sound startles him. Thud, thud, thud—raindrops pound the thirsty desert sand. Heavy rain falls on the desert only a few times each year, and this is Spadey's signal to move. Digging as fast as he can, he climbs upward and bursts from the earth. He likes the feel of warm desert rain on his speckled brown back.

Both hungry and happy, he begins his big, long meal by eating a grasshopper. He stuffs himself with beetles, ants, and flies. This dinner must last him through the next nine months of sleep.

Spadey spots a pond in a nearby hollow place. Other toads are hopping toward it. Having been alone for so long, he thinks this is a perfect place to find a friend!

Just as he gets to the pond, another male spadefoot toad puffs out his throat and makes a loud barking call. Spadey can do that too. Out goes his throat as he forces air over his voice box. Thin bands, called vocal cords, vibrate back and forth. He croaks a low tone that has special meaning for toads—a love song—and he hopes that a female toad will hear him. Soon all the male

toads are singing together until the desert is filled with their voices. What a loud noise they make!

Something within them, called instinct, says, "You've only a few hours to find your mates. The rain will soon stop. Hurry, for the water will sink into the hot sand." The desert is alive with hopping toads coming up from the wet ground. For one or two nights while the earth remains wet, hundreds of spadefoot toads fill the air with their calls, which sound something like "Baa," when you pinch your nose.

As Spadey sings, he watches. His sharp eyes spot a female hopping toward the water. She's busy eating and doesn't look at him, but Spadey sings on. When she finally jumps into the water, Spadey acts fast. He hugs her with his feet and clings to her back. As she begins to lay her eggs in the water, he covers them with his sperm. She may lay as many as 1,000 eggs. Other male toads find their mates.

Soon the bottom of the little pond is covered with tiny eggs in the form of long strings of jelly that look like strings of beads in the water. But neither Spadey nor his mate pay any attention to their eggs. Both only want to keep on eating. They even forget about each other. Time and again Spadey's long tongue zips out from its front hinge. Gulp! A tasty beetle is gone. Gulp again! Insects of all kinds—worms, snails, even millipedes—disappear like lightning.

20

The morning after the heavy rain, the sun once again shines hot from a cloudless sky. Spadey knows that hungry birds and animals might eat him before he can fill his own tummy. Hiding underneath the spines of a cactus, he has a strange, surprised look because of the vertical pupils in his eyes. His long sticky tongue, hooked onto the front of his mouth, flips out and a cricket disappears. In a split second, several ants and a grasshopper are added to his meal. He might have eaten for several hours, but his sharp ears hear the cry of a hawk. Will its keen eyes find him under the cactus?

Afraid, Spadey begins to burrow backward, using the hornlike spades on his hind feet to shove the sand and gravel aside. Swish. Swish. Just as his nose sinks below the sand, he feels the touch of sharp claws reaching down to grab him. But he's safe, and he rests until his fear goes away. Then he burrows backward down, down into the cool, moist sand. Hiding deep under the ground with a full tummy, Spadey sleeps again.

He will never see his babies when they become wiggling tadpoles in the muddy pool. But under the hot sun spadefoot toad eggs hatch fast—in only a day or two. Other kinds of toad eggs take about three or four days or more to hatch into tadpoles. Trouble comes fast to the tadpoles. Danger lurks from every direction. If the birds or animals don't eat them, their home will vanish as the sun evaporates the water.

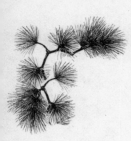

Word gets around in the desert, "Find easy-to-get meals in every mud puddle." A large, slender, brown-and-white bird dashes back and forth on long legs. Rushing madly, he seems to be going in all directions at once. The roadrunner doesn't act like a bird, because he'd rather run than fly. He's chasing a lizard that's trying to escape. With lightning speed he stabs it with his pointed bill. When he lifts his head with feathers standing straight up on top, he has a large lizard hanging from his long beak.

Now he spots a puddle where the tadpoles have already sprouted legs. Their constant wiggling has thickened the shallow water into thin mud. What a feast! With each peck he stabs a fat tadpole. What fun for the roadrunner, but not for the tadpoles! Peck. Peck. Peck. His sword-like bill rarely, if ever, misses. Since the little tadpoles have no place to hide, the mud puddle is soon empty. The roadrunner has eaten them all. The hollow where Spadey's babies hatched has more water than the smaller puddles. Maybe the roadrunner's stomach couldn't hold any more, because he runs in the other direction.

The little tadpoles grow quickly, getting legs like their parents in 10 to 15 days and changing into small spadefoot toads. That's speedy, since it takes most baby toads six weeks before they can leave the water. Once they lose their tadpole tail and grow their little digging tool, the few babies still

alive search for shade and food. Feeding on small insects, they eat until they can hold no more. Then like their parents, they dig in a backward circle down to where it's cool. Away from the desert heat, they fall asleep until next summer's rainfall.

Look, Dad, here's a dried up mud puddle filled with tiny dead tadpoles. So many died. Makes me wonder if any lived to become toads."

Dad looked thoughtful. "Yes, son, but only those who burrowed deep into the sand. Reminds me of Jesus' words when He said that only a remnant—some, not all—will be saved when He comes." Kenny stood up and looked toward the blue sky. "You know, Dad, this desert has given me a message from Jesus I could never have learned at church. Those little toads had so many enemies. The only ones who lived were those who hid deep in the ground. I think I'd better follow their example and hide in Jesus. Only then can I be safe from the enemies that Satan brings in my way."

Dad put his arm around Kenny's shoulder. Both felt the presence of the Lord, as Kenny whispered, "I choose to ask Jesus each day to keep me from sin and evil."

3

Adventure in the Snow

When Kenny and his dad left the desert, they climbed to 9,000 feet around Mount San Jacinto, the first snow-capped peak of their trip.

"We've hiked 135 miles from the Mexican border. How do you like backpacking?" Dad asked as they prepared freeze-dried food for supper.

"I'll admit that hiking this trail is harder than I thought. But I'm getting tougher. My muscles aren't so sore anymore. My pack's *beginning* to feel good on my shoulders. Even the blisters on my heels are healing, though they still hurt a little."

"I'm beginning to feel like a real hiker now that we've set up a routine for most hiking days. Let's talk about it," Dad suggested.

"I'm so tired each night I like going to bed early. And waking up early gives us a chance to start hiking in the cool morning before it gets hot."

"I notice you're more than ready for a big breakfast— usually granola, powdered milk, and dried fruit, plus a power bar. After we have our worship, we break camp and hit the trail hard."

"Yeah, I feel full of energy when we start, but by noon I'm eager for our long break for lunch."

"Lunch doesn't take much preparation. Are you satisfied with bouillon or a soup mix plus crackers, honey, and peanut butter? And, of course, the snacks of more dried fruit, nuts, seeds, dates, and raisins or trail mix?"

"Sure am, and I'm ready for rest or a nap—maybe even a swim if there's water nearby. Lots better to clean up in the middle of the day when it's warmer. Brrr. These mountain streams and lakes are cold!"

Dad, always a detail man, continued recounting their routine. "Usually we hike into the evening since the days are long, leaving enough time for a supper. This is varied. Sometimes we have corn or wheat spaghetti with Parmesan cheese. Tortillas and rice are good, too. Occasionally we do enjoy the more expensive freeze-dried casseroles and green beans or peas, with powdered gravy. To really enjoy weeks of strenuous hiking, every hiker needs good food plus extras for variety. What changes would you like? Or are you satisfied?"

"Suits me fine, Dad, especially when we have a few treats like an orange, granola bar, or some candy."

Before they started eating, Dad began to rub his bare arms. "I'm getting chilled. I think we'd better take off our cut-offs and tee-shirts. In this altitude we need warm pants, a wool shirt, and a down jacket tonight. Feels like winter up here."

"Yeah. Brrr." After changing his clothes, Kenny said, "Dad, . . . you know what I like best?"

"What?"

"Hunting for a campsite each night. We take our time to choose a place with level ground to pitch our tent, and we make sure there's water nearby. Of course, it must have an inspiring view, too. Then we enjoy a nice warm supper and talk a while. Sometimes if it's cold, we have a campfire. After we get settled it seems like home, except I miss Mom."

"So do I," Dad added. "Wouldn't she love to watch that sunset over the mountains with us?"

The next morning they climbed steep switchbacks. The higher they climbed, the more slippery the trail got. Soon several feet of snow covered the trail. As Kenny stepped from a rock onto the sloping snow, his feet slipped, and the shifting weight of his pack threw him off balance. He slid a dozen feet downhill before he stopped.

"Kenny, are you OK?" Dad called.

"Yeah, I think so. Are my trousers ripped?"

"Let's see."

Kenny turned around, and his dad brushed him off. "No, you're all in one piece." Then Dad explained, "I think I know how we can cross these snow fields safely. Watch what I do. See how I chop a narrow ledge in the snow with the outside edge of my right boot?" Dad demonstrated. "Then I put my weight on it. Next, with the inside edge of my left boot I make another cut."

Kenny followed. "Works great, but the going's slow."

Hours later they came to a fast-flowing stream. Dad opened the map and studied it for several minutes. "No wonder they call it White Water River! I'm afraid our crossing's going to be cold and wet. This river's twice its normal size. I can barely see the logs that we'd use if it were low water. Kenny, if I tie a rope around your waist and mine, are you willing to wade through that icy water?"

"Isn't there another way?" he objected. "Let's look around first. You go upstream, and I'll look downstream."

They did, but they couldn't find a better place to cross.

"Sorry, Kenny. Before we attempt a crossing, I'll throw

a rope loop across the stream and hook it on that stump over there. We'll make this end firm by putting a large rock on it. Then we can yank it loose when we're safe on the other side."

Kenny watched while Dad tied a slip knot and began to throw the loop. He made it on the third attempt. "OK. Let's take off our pants, tie our boots to the top of my pack, and plunge in." Dad began to loosen his boot laces.

"I'm scared, Dad. Let's pray first."

Kenny asked Jesus to send His angels to help them. Then shivering both from fear and cold, he held onto Dad with one hand and the rope with the other hand. The swift water knocked him off balance once, but Dad hung on tight. When the water reached Dad's waist, Kenny felt it gurgling about his neck. His pack even got wet. Was he ever glad when his feet touched the other side!

"Looks like the river's flowing into that lake. We can camp beside it and dry out. As soon as you change into dry clothes, hunt for firewood so that we can get warm. We mustn't take a chance. Many hikers freeze to death in the mountains and die of hypothermia."

Kenny scrounged around for wood while Dad prepared some shavings with his pocket knife. Soon they had a fire going, and their wet clothes were draped on bushes near the heat. But they couldn't rest yet. After they pitched their tent and had eaten supper, they huddled close to the fire. "Doesn't this feel great to be warm again! Can't say I enjoyed that icy mountain stream. You did real well during the crossing, Kenny. I'm proud of you."

"Thanks, Dad." Kenny felt good receiving Dad's approval.

"To think just a few days ago we were sweating in the desert heat! Aren't the trees pretty, mirrored upside down in the lake?" Dad's photographic eye found pictures everywhere.

"Look!" Kenny blurted. "What's that? Something's moving over there." He pointed through the pines to the lakeshore. Two huge Canada geese waddled into full view. The black-and-white birds, honking softly to each other, showed no fear of their human visitors.

"Sure wish I knew their life story," Kenny thought aloud.

Gandy Brings Martha Home

A flock of more than 100 Canada geese rise from the marshes of the northland. The cold winds and shortening amounts of daylight tell them that winter is on its way— time to leave their summer home, where their babies have grown to full-size geese. Now high in the sky, they begin to form into a tight V for their long and dangerous trip south. With a tail wind to push them, they fly 35 to 40 miles an hour nonstop for 12 hours before stopping for food and rest.

Gandy, a male, takes the lead place. The tips of his wings make the air go up, which helps the birds behind. Each flies slightly to the outside of the bird ahead. Because the lead bird tires quickly, they change leaders often.

Shortly before they stop for rest, Pretty Girl, Gandy's lifetime mate, takes the lead. As she guides them to their first stop, she has no idea that below is her greatest enemy—far worse than storms or hurricanes. Instead, she sees other geese, some resting safely on a pond of water, others feeding in a corn field. She doesn't know that they are decoys made of plastic or carved from wood and that an enemy has placed them there. From 3,000 feet up, she can't see the hidden hunters crouching with their shotguns on their shoulders.

Pretty Girl slows down and flaps her wings, which sends a signal back through the flock. They follow her as she coasts closer to the ground. The geese honk loudly, eager to land and feed. Just to be sure all is safe, she makes a wide circle, checking again for danger. The fields lie silent, so she sets her wings to land. Tired, she'll be happy to feed and let a new leader take them farther south.

Pretty Girl is only a few feet above the field when the hunters open fire. She's the first to fall as the buckshot knocks her out of the air. Others around her tumble to the ground, helpless. Crying and beating their wings, the other geese try to fly upward to escape, but more geese fall as additional shots ring out. Crack! Bang! It is all terribly

frightening, and Gandy takes over, honking commands as he again forms the flock into its V. Higher and higher he takes the rest of the geese.

Gandy looks down at his lifetime mate and utters a loud, sad cry. She lies still, blood oozing from her warm body. He keeps crying as he guides the flock away from the awful scene.

Though tired, they continue flying until they come to a wildlife refuge. They see thousands of other geese in the air, on the water, in the marshlands. Without fear they join the others in this safe place, where hunters are not allowed to come. Here they rest and feed for more than a week before they start out again to their winter home.

Every year Gandy comes to this same place. But this time, lonesome without his mate, he hunts for another. For three days he looks for just the right goose for him. Then he sees her standing at the edge of the water in marsh grass. Will she accept him?

Slowly he walks toward her, reaches out, and touches his bill to hers. Martha lowers her head.

At that moment Gandy sees another gander just four feet away, swimming toward him with wings raised. He, too, wants Martha for his mate. Gandy stretches his long neck, points his bill like a spear, and rushes angrily toward the male goose. He beats his wings, hitting the other goose hard with the bony outer edge and knocking him into the water. Squawking, the other bird flies away, and Gandy honks triumphantly.

Turning toward Martha, he makes soft sounds and then puts his neck and head close to the ground, swaying it back and forth. As he gets close to her he opens his bill, rustles his feathers, and talks to her. She, too, opens her bill, fluffs her feathers, and waits. He comes closer, brushing gently against her.

Will Martha say "Yes" to Gandy? He'll soon find out, because he turns and walks away. Martha follows him, honking. He takes off across the marshlands, and she follows close behind. From now on wherever he goes, she follows. When he naps by the water, she snuggles close beside him. They'll stay together as long as they both live.

Winter is like a vacation for Gandy and Martha. They stay with the flock, feeding on both grass and grain. Together they oil their black-and-white feathers to keep them light, waterproof, and warm. Often she hears his loving call that sounds like, "Come, come, come."

One evening in late March Gandy, with Martha right behind him, heads for his home in the north where he was born. Once again he takes the lead, the rest of the flock forming the V behind him. They don't hurry but often stop for food and rest. Somehow the geese seem to know that hunting season is closed and no guns will shoot them. They feed in fields close

to farms as they look for spilled corn.

One evening the wind blows strong, bringing bitter cold—and snow, which covers the food, so the flock huddle together in a pasture to wait out the storm. For several days they hunt for corn stalks to eat, until the sun returns to warm the land. When they head north again, another goose takes the lead.

As they fly over high mountains, Gandy seems to know just where he is. Below he spots a little lake, and he lets out a loud cry of joy. He breaks out of formation, and Martha follows. Circling several times, he honks his happiness. This is his summer home, the place where he was born and where he and Pretty Girl had raised their young. Now he and Martha will begin their search for a place to build their nest. The nest must be built on solid ground, be hidden from enemies, yet be where the geese can watch for danger. They also need to nest near open water with grass and plants for the babies to eat.

After Gandy and Martha mate, she builds her nest from marsh grass, twigs, and branches. Pulling the down from her breast, she makes the nest soft and warm. About an hour after it is built, she lays her first egg. Every day and a half after that she lays another dull white egg and pulls more down from her breast to cover it. After laying nine eggs, she has a bare spot where her skin touches the eggs, keeping them warm.

Gandy stays close by like a soldier on guard duty. If any animal or bird comes close, he lowers his head and hisses in anger. For 25 to 28 days Gandy stays near, and Martha leaves her nest only to get food and water. She turns the eggs often to keep the little sack that holds the chick from sticking to the shell.

One evening Gandy notices a coyote sneaking through the trees on the far side of the lake. Martha sees him, too. She's ready to fight with her powerful wings if he comes near the nest. Brave Gandy flies across the lake and lands in the shallow water. Hissing loudly, his head low, he swims toward the coyote. Slowly the coyote slinks back into the woods.

Two days before the eggs hatch, Martha hears peeping sounds from her eggs. Each unborn gosling, the name for baby geese, has a sharp egg tooth on the tip of its tiny black bill, which it uses to crack the shell. After the first crack, it takes the baby two long days of hard work to break its way out. It looks like a mess, a little ball of slick, wet feathers.

Seven of the nine eggs hatch. Martha and Gandy stay close by the babies until their yellow, downy feathers dry. Their sharp black eyes open at birth, so as soon as they're dry, they join their mother and father to hunt for food.

The babies look cute and cuddly when Gandy proudly takes them to the water. Martha stays in the back, keeping her little ones between her and Gandy. Whatever

their parents do, the goslings copy. They soon learn to tip up their tails and bob for food beneath the shallow water of the lake.

On their second day, while they paddle close to shore, a large snapping turtle spies the little family. Quickly it swims underwater and grabs the leg of one gosling. "Peep, peep," the baby screams, but before Gandy can come to the rescue, the turtle pulls it underneath the water. Now there are only six.

Both Martha and Gandy keep constant watch for other enemies. At any time an owl, hawk, or eagle might swoop from the sky and grab a baby in its talons. When the goslings are 2 weeks old and their feathers begin to appear, a great blue heron, hidden in the tall cattails, spots a gosling nearby. Just before his sharp beak stabs it, Gandy squawks, diverting the heron's attention while the baby swims to safety.

During the warm summer months, Gandy and Martha spend each day teaching their babies how Canada geese can live safely. They swim with them and teach them how to fly, how to find food, and how to watch for enemies. Now the babies are getting as big as their parents.

Once again the leaves begin to turn color and the nights get cool and then cold. Gandy and Martha watch the clouds in the sky. Other geese land on the lake. Then one October night when the moon is full, Gandy and Martha know it's time to make the long flight to their winter home. The six young geese join their parents as they leave the marshlands and take to the air, honking, honking, honking. They form into a V as the family starts south through the night.

Whder Kenny woke up the next morning, Dad had restarted the fire. "Special treat this morning. Pancakes are ready."

"Whoopee! Sounds good. I want to get a drink first," Kenny said as he tipped his water bottle for a drink. "Dad, it's frozen solid!"

"I know. Mine was too. Winter's not over in the high country, is it? The higher we go, the deeper the snow. With swollen rivers and snow getting deeper all the time, I think we need to check with a ranger about the trail conditions in the high Sierras. Maybe it's safer for us to leave the Crest Trail at Big Bear and call Mom to come get us. While we spend a few weeks at home, I hope the snow will melt."

"OK with me, Dad." Kenny helped fold the tent and sleeping bag. "Before we leave, I want to take a closer look at the Canada geese. Look, one is standing by the shore!"

They walked toward him. He lowered his head and began to hiss.

"Good gander, on the job guarding your mate," Dad said, smiling his approval. "You know, Kenny, if we could learn to do our jobs as faithfully as that gander does, we'd be a lot happier."

Kenny thought a moment. "You couldn't be hinting about

35

a son of yours who doesn't always get his chores done, could you? Maybe if you'd call me 'Good gander,' I might remember him and keep at my jobs till they're done."

"Good boy!" Dad smiled again as he messed up Kenny's hair. "Now let's start down the trail."

When they reached the ranger station, the ranger informed them, "This is a record year for snowfall. California's Sierra Nevada mountains have more than 15 feet of snow covering the trail. Even with snowshoes and by carefully climbing over the much deeper drifts, I doubt that you could find your way. Many trail markers will be covered. You"ll never be able to reach the highest point of the trail, 13,200 feet above sea level. Sorry, but this section of the Pacific Crest Trail through Sequoia, King's Canyon, and Yosemite will be closed for sometime yet."

Kenny looked disappointed. "Hiking is still great, Dad. We've had fun stopping to watch the animals and birds. And we'd never be able to see the plants and wildflowers under all that snow. Maybe we can come back and do that section another year."

"Good idea. You can be sure the plants and animals will be far different when the trail drops to near sea level on the Oregon-Washington border," Dad said.

Kenny's dream of living in the wilderness far from the sounds of the city had come true. He loved the silence, when all he could hear was the crunch of his boots or water gurgling in a tiny mountain stream.

One night Kenny had whispered from his sleeping bag, "It's great to fall asleep in this quiet world of tall pine trees and huge rocks. The stars look so close that I almost feel like I could reach up and touch one. Thanks, Dad, for hiking with me on the Pacific Crest Trail."

4

Mountain Surprise

Kenny and his Dad enjoyed the luxuries of home. Mom's good food, hot showers, and soft beds seemed great, but just being with Mom and Heather was the best. One evening two weeks later Dad announced, "I think I can take another break from the office. I called the ranger station today, and the snow's still too heavy in the Mt. Whitney area. We'll have to skip this highest point on the trail and go into Yosemite. Might be better to try that rugged area when you're a bit older."

Kenny looked disappointed. "Come look at the map, son. Maybe we could tackle the section through Desolation Wilderness to Donner Pass. Still pretty high and there's lots of snow. Anybody interested?" Dad smiled at Kenny.

"You bet! Can Mom take us tomorrow morning? Is the wilderness as desolate as it sounds?" Kenny picked up his backpack, which had been ready for days. They'd learned by experience that efficient hikers do better with lighter packs.

"Yes, the wilderness is desolate, but I can't get away from the office until tomorrow afternoon. Don't forget your snowshoes! The ranger said that parts of the trail might be covered with up to 13 feet of snow. That could be rough going. Might have to navigate with our compass and maps."

After several hours of driving, they came to the trail-head. "Goodbye, Mom. Thanks for all the things you're doing to make this fun," Kenny said as he hugged her.

"Wow, it's great to be back in the forest again with a pack on my back!" Kenny let out a whoop of joy.

That night they camped at Lake Aloha in Desolation Valley. "You're right, Dad. This place seems spooky! Only a few trees here and there against a wall of bare rock on the far side of the water." Kenny looked toward the lake. "Look! There must be hundreds of rock islands."

"And all the same gray granite rock like the mountains," Dad pointed to the valley.

Finally the last embers of the campfire lost their glow. Kenny dumped a bucket of water on the ashes just to be sure the fire wouldn't flare up unexpectedly. Soon both tired hikers were fast asleep in their "mummy-bags."

The next morning after breakfast they broke camp and got ready for another long hike. As they climbed, the snow got deeper, and they soon sank in up to their knees.

"Time to stop and put on your snowshoes," Dad instructed. "Without them we'll soon be in up to our waists. The snow banks are going to be real deep around Heather Lake. I hope we can follow the trail."

At first Kenny had a hard time walking on "shoes" that were three feet long and one and a half feet wide, but he soon learned to make an outward motion with each step as he slid along the surface of the snow.

"Dad, I haven't seen the trail signs for a long time," Kenny said as they stopped to rest.

"Nor have I. Let's take out the map again. Maybe we can find where we are," Dad agreed. "These drifts are so high I fear the signs are covered."

With map in hand they backtracked and tried several routes that looked like they might be trails. Each time they had to stop before fast-flowing streams, which were too deep or dangerous to cross. Then they came to what looked like a river. Finally Dad shook his head. "I fear we've lost the trail. Our navigation skills aren't good enough to find it. One thing I know. The map indicates that this large river flows into Lake Tahoe. If we follow it, we'll find our way out."

"Looks awful to me! One wrong step in crossing that icy torrent and we'd be dead." Kenny looked scared.

"But we can make our way along the banks. It will be tough on snowshoes, but we'll drop rapidly in elevation. When we get out of the snow near Lake Tahoe, we'll find the trail again."

So they trudged on, stopping often to rest. Leaning his pack against a big boulder, Dad suggested, "We might as well enjoy this magnificent wilderness. So silent and lovely. Let's see how many sounds we can hear."

Kenny sat on a large rock nearby. Neither spoke for several minutes as the wind blew into their faces. He heard the "yank, yank" of a nuthatch, the cheery call of the chickadee, and the "caw" of a crow that flew overhead. The music of the wind through the pines floated in the background.

Suddenly a large cat with a head that seemed too small for its long, tan body poked around the boulder. It had short, heavy legs, a long tail tipped in black, and pointed ears. For a moment it stared at them with beautiful almond-shaped eyes. Then in a flash it leaped over the rock into the forest.

Kenny gasped! His heart pounded so hard he could feel it in his throat. "Was—was that a mountain lion?" he whispered.

"You bet it was! Few people ever get to see one in the wild like that!" Dad was as excited as Kenny. "Some people call them cougars or panthers. They're experts at keeping out of sight, in spite of their big size. Can you see why they're also called the ghost cat?"

"Yeah, it came so quietly and was gone so fast! Look at the paw prints in the snow!" They bent down to examine them.

"Must be five inches across," Dad guessed. "The pad of its foot made the large oval, and the four smaller ones are toes. Needs big feet to slip silently through the forest."

"Dad, I've heard that mountain lions attack people. But this one seemed afraid and got away fast. What are the chances of it coming back and getting us?"

"Most people don't understand the cougar," Dad said sadly. "Hunters enjoy killing them. People like to run them down with snowmobiles, followed by dogs that chase them into a tree. Then they shoot them and call it sport."

"I wish we could follow that lion and see how it lives," Kenny said.

Felis, the Mountain Lion

Felis has spent her first two years of life with her mother, who has given her love, food, and warmth. But now the mother lion tries to drive her from the food. When Felis

40

wants to play, her mother hits her hard with her paw, snarling and biting. Felis can't understand why mother lion has changed. She doesn't know that her mother wants to mate again and have a new family.

Finally Felis leaves, alone and hungry. Where will she find a new home? Mother lion has taught her how to hunt small animals— mice, squirrels, rabbits, and even porcupines. But she's never caught the animal that is her main food—deer.

Felis stops at a canyon. Looking down she sees a lake with a buck deer feeding. She knows she's no match for him. Her first deer kills will have to be either the very young or the very old. Hoping this area might make a good home, she climbs the mountain above the lake. But Felis meets another mountain lion, who snarls at her. In mountain lion language this means "This is my home. You must go." Felis understands and leaves.

She silently pads her way down the steep mountain. Hearing the sound of a stream, she heads for it, hoping to find a rabbit among the willow trees. She comes upon a clearing where a forest fire had burned years ago. Not far away, she sees an old doe feeding. Slowly Felis inches her way forward, stopping when the deer looks up. Closer and closer she creeps. Her tail twitches just like a tabby cat stalking a sparrow. Then Felis charges. The old doe never knew what hit her!

Felis drags her catch to the edge of the

clearing. Then she does what she'd seen her mother do. She rips out the doe's stomach and intestines. Otherwise the meat will taste bad from the doe's half-digested food and stomach acids. Felis eats the heart, liver, and lungs. Then she covers the dead animal with dirt and leaves to keep the flies away. The next day she returns to eat again. When she has her fill, she covers it again and climbs to a flat rock above the clearing to sleep.

Felis chooses to make this her home. She's far away from humans, her greatest enemies. Maybe here no hunter will find her footprints. That evening she goes back once again to eat and sees a small animal tearing meat from her deer. With a leap she starts for him. The fox hears her coming and runs into the forest. Then he circles back to watch her through the trees. After Felis has eaten, she covers the carcass again and leaves. The fox comes back to finish his meal when she disappears.

Often she wanders far from her clearing, sometimes traveling as far as 20 miles in a night. One afternoon she comes upon some scratch marks on a tree where another cougar had sharpened its claws. Later she sees a big male mountain lion drinking by a stream. This is his home, so she keeps her distance.

When December comes, Felis feels a new desire inside her. She roams the forest, mewing low, deep sounds, calling for a mate. She returns to the area where the male cougar lives. She rubs against the markings he's left on bushes, rocks, and trees. One night she raises her voice in a wild scream, telling other lions she is near. The male hears her scream and follows the trail she left. He stays with her for two weeks. After they mate, he returns to his home. He'll never help in the care and feeding of the cubs she'll have.

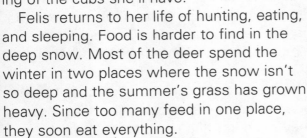

Felis returns to her life of hunting, eating, and sleeping. Food is harder to find in the deep snow. Most of the deer spend the winter in two places where the snow isn't so deep and the summer's grass has grown heavy. Since too many feed in one place, they soon eat everything.

Felis helps solve the problem by scattering the herd to other places and killing an old buck, which leaves more food for the others. Little by little they come back to the willow area. By February all the very young or very old deer are gone, and those who remain become harder to get.

All her waking hours Felis searches for food for herself and the unborn cubs within her body. After almost a week of no food, she remembers a fox's den. Maybe she'll find a small animal there. She climbs up a ledge and pushes her way through a narrow opening between two large rocks. Back into the cave she searches. Nothing.

Outside again, she hears the familiar grunt of a porcupine. She finds him gnawing

on the bark of a fir tree. Too hungry to wait
for it to come down, she climbs to a branch
nearby. The porcupine turns its back, quills
erect, and swings its tail. One touch would
load Felis' paws or face with quills. How can
she knock it off the branch without touching
that tail? She jumps onto the same branch,
a few feet from the porcupine. The weight
of the two animals is too much. With a loud
crack it breaks, and both fall into the snow.
Quickly Felis jumps to her feet and sees the
porcupine walking away. Bounding toward
him, she flips him onto his back. That night
she falls to sleep with a full stomach.

In March Felis begins to search for a den
or cave where her cubs will be safe when
they are born. She remembers the empty
fox's den. It's just right. Dry and protected
from the weather, its only opening is
through the narrow place between the
rocks. Felis moves in. Late in March three
little balls of fur, each about 12 inches long
and weighing one pound, are born. There
are two females and one male, and they are
covered with black spots. She licks the
newborn cubs until they are slick and clean.
The babies can't open their eyes, but they
find their way to her nipples and suck as
hard as they can.

At two weeks their eyes open. After four
weeks the cubs have grown to five pounds
each. Felis takes them outside on the ledge
to play. They jump and run and play rough-
and-tumble games together. Best of all they

like the tail game. Felis moves her tail back and forth, and the cubs grab it, hang onto it, jump at it. This is their first lesson in how to hunt. Whenever she leaves to find food, she hides them inside the den for safety.

By early May Felis stops giving her cubs milk. When she brings a rabbit to the den, they pull it from three directions. In her loving, stern way she settles their fight. Now at 10 pounds each, they've outgrown the den. They're ready to see the big world around them.

Everything in the forest is new and exciting to them. They nose fir cones, climb over fallen logs, and look into every hole in the ground. The male has fun hiding. When one of his sisters passes, he jumps out and springs onto her. Soon they learn to pounce on insects, and later they even catch a mouse.

All summer Felis gives her cubs hunting lessons. They learn new tricks each day. After they fill their stomachs, she takes them to the large rock where she likes to lie in the sun while they sleep in the bushes below her. She often looks far away into the valley toward the home of the man she fears, a rancher with his hunting dogs.

She doesn't know that he's seen her footprints and those of her cubs and that he'll get money for every cougar he kills. She doesn't know that he's tied one of his dogs to the bushes near the rock, planning to get her. The dog is asleep when Felis

climbs up on the boulder and the cubs slink into the bushes. The male cub almost steps on the dog, which awakes with a yip! The cub leaps back, but the dog grabs him. The female cubs flee.

With one huge leap, Felis is on the dog. She frees her cub and claws the dog once. Leaving it dead, she and her cubs race over the mountain, through streams and marshes, to the clearing. Here they hide for a week.

Finally hunger forces them to go where the deer feed. The hunting is good, and she takes down an old buck. The family eat their fill. Then she covers it with dirt and branches and leads her cubs back to the rock, where they sleep. Late that afternoon they return to feed again. The two female cubs trot ahead. At the edge of the clearing Felis stops. She sniffs the air and smells that awful odor. Man and dogs!

Calling her cubs, instantly she turns and runs up the hill. The male obeys, but the females run to the deer meat. From the far end of the meadow come the hounds, running straight for the two cougar cubs. Behind them follows the rancher with his gun.

The cubs turn to run after their mother. Where is she? Dashing to the trees, they try to get away. But the dogs close in. So they climb into a tree. With eyes large from fear, the cubs look down at the barking, leaping dogs. Moments later, the rancher arrives. From far away Felis and the male cub hear those awful sounds, *bang! bang!* Two little animals fall to the ground.

Felis continues to teach her one cub how to live safely in the wilderness far from people. He learns all the skills of hunting. The spots of babyhood fade away. By the time he is 2 years old, he is as big as his mother, ready to find his own home and live on his own.

'll treasure that memory of our brief encounter with a mountain lion as long as I live!" Kenny said.

"So will I. But we'd better trudge on over the snow-banks toward Lake Tahoe."

The two hikers had never felt more tired. Kenny dropped to the ground. "Sliding on snowshoes up and down steep drifts is hard work!" he gasped.

"Keep trying, Kenny. I think we're nearing the lake. The snow is getting less."

They hiked for several more hours, when Kenny gave a whoop of delight. "There it is! And we can take off these clumsy things."

In a short time they found the familiar rounded triangle, the trail's official emblem.

"Let's thank God for caring for us while we were lost," Dad said.

The trail took them through the mountains west of Lake Tahoe, past Squaw Valley, to Donner Pass. North of the pass they came within a few miles of abandoned

gold camps and old mining towns like Poker Flat and
Gold Lake.

That evening Dad said, "I need to call the office, son.
In about 20 miles we'll come to the north fork of the
Feather River. Not far off the trail is the little town of
Beldon on highway 70. I'm sure Mom has sent us some
care packages there. Are you willing to take a short break
into civilization?"

"You bet I am! 'Twas tough going on snowshoes, but
that mountain lion made it worth all the cold and snow. I'll
never forget the surprised look it gave us."

"You know, Kenny," Dad spoke slowly, "the cougar
shows that God has a special plan for each of us. I wish
people understood mountain lions better. By keeping the
food supply in balance, they help other wild animals—and
us, too. Wouldn't life be great if everyone looked for the
good in others—both animals and people?"

"You're right, Dad. Reminds me of a verse I learned in
Sabbath school: 'Judge not, that ye be not judged.' I'm
sorry I misjudged the cougar by listening to what others
say" (Matt. 7:1).

5

On Eagle's Wings

Sitting on a large rock, the two hikers poured over the map that dad had pulled from his backpack.

"Here's the side trail into the little town of Beldon. We'll stop at the post office and pick up the packages Mom sent. I'll call the office, and then we'll talk to her. Since the town's on the highway, I'm sure we can get a hot meal at a restaurant. Anybody interested?"

"I'll say I am! And since it's getting late, Dad, how about trying out a soft bed in a motel? Think our skin could stand hot showers instead of cold lakes?"

Dad laughed. "So you're still a bit of a city slicker! Yes, I'm sure there'll be some type of motel there. Whatever it's like, it will be an improvement over the hard ground. If they have a Laundromat facility, we might even wash our clothes. Imagine smelling clean again."

"I've got another idea, Dad. Could we mail our snowshoes, big heavy jackets, and protecting tarp home? Surely winter for us is over by now, and I'd like to travel lighter. Do you think we'll hit snow and cold as we go north now?"

"In late July there shouldn't be very much snow. Maybe a little around mounts Lassen and Shasta, but I'm sure we can push through the drifts with just our boots."

The business at the post office, the phone calls, and

washing clothes took the rest of the afternoon and evening. That night as they prepared for bed, Kenny exclaimed, "Wow! I enjoyed that meal and washing my hair in hot water. Thanks, Dad, for giving us a break, especially talking to Mom. But I'll be ready for the wilderness tomorrow."

They hit the trail early the next day, glad to leave civilization. "I love being back where we can hear the birds sing and not the roar of trucks on the highway. I'll admit the trail is tough, but I feel so much closer to God out here. And the scenery is super," Kenny said.

At the next switchback in the trail, Dad pointed to cone-shaped Mt. Lassen ahead. "How's that for beauty! Before Mount St. Helens erupted, northern California boasted that Lassen is the only active volcano within the continental United States."

"Any chance it'll blow now?"

"Don't worry. It blew last in 1915. But you'll smell sulphur at Boiling Springs Lake. Mud pots belch and gurgle, and steam rises from really hot water, 125 degrees."

The next few days they enjoyed Lassen Volcanic National Park as they hiked through beds of black lava. Not far into the park's boundary they smelled a strong sulphurous odor. Following their nose, they came upon a steaming, milky green pond ringed by cracked gray mud. The sign said "Boiling Springs Lake, 125 degrees."

Even though it was mid-summer, they had to go around snow drifts. "Brrr, it's cold! Are those snowflakes I see coming down?" Kenny shivered as he looked at Dad.

"Yep, that's snow. Those clouds look menacing—like they mean business. Could be we're in for a real storm. I wish we hadn't mailed our warm jackets and heavy sleeping bags home. We're going to be cold tonight in our lightweight mummy bags. I didn't think there'd be this much snow here!"

Ahead Kenny saw a sign "Terminal Geyser." A mist of steam from the boiling water blew toward them. "Oh, that feels good. I'm going there to get warm," Kenny jumped over the sign "Trail Closed." But Dad hesitated. The nearby parking lot was empty. All tourists had fled for warmer places. Not even a ranger in sight. The snowstorm increased. Finally Dad followed Kenny to the warmth.

"I've got an idea that'll warm us up," Kenny said. "See all that boiling water flowing from the geyser. It's running down the hill and has formed a thermal pool far from the tourist trail. I put my finger in it, and it's about the temperature of a hot tub. Maybe a bit cooler. Can't think of a better way to spend a cold night in a blizzard."

At first Dad shook his head. "What would the ranger say if he found a couple of hikers sitting in this pool?"

"I think he'd rather find us warm and alive, than freezing to death from hypothermia. My clothes are already soaked, so all I'll have to do is take off my boots and socks and get in. Besides it's almost dark, and you know there'll be no one looking at thermal activity tonight. We've got this section of the park to ourselves."

Dad, also chilled to the bone, finally agreed. With their backs leaning on warm rocks, they enjoyed the warmth. But the snowstorm didn't stop when dawn came, so they stayed in the pool. Getting out long enough to eat and care for their toilet needs, they kept returning to nature's bathtub. The heavy snow formed a curtain, and they saw no one. By late afternoon the snow stopped and the sky cleared. They left their pool, changed into dry clothes, and hiked down the road.

Several miles down the road, they met a ranger standing

by his pickup. After Dad had asked for weather information and directions, Kenny came up.

"Sir, what would happen if a person sat in one of those thermal pools?"

"The hot mineral water isn't good for the skin. The mineral salts could scorch him like a burn. Why do you ask?" the ranger said.

Kenny grinned. "We're hiking the Pacific Crest Trail. Dad and I got caught in the blizzard last night without all our warm gear. To keep from freezing, we spent the night and part of today in a pool near Terminal Geyser."

The ranger didn't look happy. Trying to look stern, he finally said, "That's why we put up No Trespassing signs. But since it was dark, maybe you couldn't read it." Then he smiled, "Don't blame us if your skin gets red and tender."

"Thanks, Sir, just wanted you to know. Dad's a doctor. Maybe he can fix whatever happens." Kenny felt better having confessed.

Not long after they left the park boundary, they rounded a bend and there, still 75 miles away, rose the huge snow-covered pyramid of Mt. Shasta towering 10,000 feet above the rest of the area.

They saw it again and again from different parts of the Crest Trail. "Wow! It's more majestic each time. Seems like an old friend!" Kenny exclaimed.

"According to the Crest Trail guidebook, we'll get glimpses of it for the next 350 hiking miles. But it's not the only friend we've got. Look, there's another! The king of the air!" Dad pointed to a white-headed eagle soaring above them. Its snowy head and tail contrasted with its dark brown body.

"I thought bald eagles were rare. How come we see them so often?"

"That's because we're hiking where they live. Look at that huge wingspan. Must be seven or eight feet," Dad spread his arms out like the bird. "What a great symbol for our nation!"

"Yeah! Its picture's on the seal of the United States and also on the one-dollar bill."

"How'd you know that?" Dad asked with surprise.

"From school, but I've sure learned a lot more about birds and animals hiking this trail than in science class! Don't think I ever studied about the bald eagle."

"Let's sit down and watch it."

Hali, the Bald Eagle

Perched on the highest limb of the tallest tree, Hali sits very still as he keeps guard over his mate and nest. His keen eyes scan the mountain and the lake. With eyes like a telescope, he sees a fish more than a mile away come to the surface of the water. His eyes can adjust from far to near like a self-focusing camera. In seconds he's in the air and intends to catch that fish. All the time

during his long, slanting dive, he has the fish in focus. Swooping down at a speed of almost 100 miles an hour, he brakes by spreading his wings and tail in an aerial skid stop. Coming to a halt in the space of 20 feet, he grabs the fish in his talons and soars back to his nest.

No other bird loves its home like bald eagles. Though they may live as long as 30 or 40 years, eagle couples return to the same nest, usually built on the top of a tall tree or a cliff. In the spring their first job is to repair it. As a result the nest grows bigger and deeper. One old nest in a tree that blew down weighed two tons and was 20 feet deep.

Hali and his mate, Leuco, will stay together for life. Hali was 5 years old when he began to court Leuco. To win her he showed real flying talent. The two birds flew so high in the air that a person on the ground could barely see them. Then Hali rolled over and flew upside down, stretching his yellow claws out over his stomach. This meant "Come join me." Leuco swooped close and hooked her talons in his, locking them together. The two birds spread their wings and did cartwheels over and over toward the earth. They tumbled through the sky at top speed, real acrobats. Just before they'd crash to the earth, they broke apart. Back up again, they did it again and again.

Until then neither of them had a home. Together they chose the site. Hali brought the foundation, big sticks about six feet long and two inches across. He's so good at flying that he doesn't need to land. Swooping close to the ground, he picked up the sticks with his talons. Hali saw a branch he needed that was still part of a tree. Flying at full speed, he hit it with his feet, and grabbed it as it cracked and broke away.

Leuco built the nest by fitting the sticks on a platform of tree branches. Hali brought more sticks until she made it two feet deep and about five feet across. Next he carried sod, weeds, moss, soft grass, lichens, and feathers for Leuco to line the nest with. That took four days of hard work. Then together they flew off and brought back something green, like a branch of pine needles or a spray of leaves, laying it in the center of the nest. Only eagles know why they do this.

After they mated in the nest, Leuco laid two white eggs, not much bigger than a chicken egg. For the next 35 to 40 days father and mother took turns sitting on the eggs.

The eaglets worked hard to break through the thick egg shell, chipping away with a sharp point at the end of their beak. They came out of the egg with tiny heads of white down, eyes closed, and very thin bodies covered with gray down. The parents tore off little pieces of fish to put into the babies' open mouths. Always one parent stayed by the nest.

When the eaglets' eyes opened at three

weeks, Hali tore up the fish with his thick, hooked bill to show them how to do it. Hardly able to stand, they moved with wobbly steps as they pecked at the food he brought. Quickly they learned to tear off small pieces.

Soon dark brown, almost black, feathers replaced the down. When Leuco dropped a whole fish in the nest, the eaglets tore it apart themselves. Like children play with toys, the eaglets played with the sticks in the nest. Hali and Leuco taught them to jump up and down and flap their wings. They loved this game and played by the hours. This was their preflight training.

The eaglets are now 10 weeks old and are as large as their parents. No wonder home seems crowded. This means it's time to leave the nest. Scared, the eaglets flutter to the edge, but tumble back in as fast as they can. Their parents call to them, "Try again." If they don't, Hali holds food in his beak out too far for them to reach. When at last an eaglet flies on its own, it gets a reward of food.

Now for the flight lessons. Their parents teach them to spread the tips of their longest wing feathers apart like fingers. By doing this they can glide without flapping their wings. With such perfect flight equipment, they learn to soar higher and higher, flying almost to 10,000 feet above the earth.

One day Hali spies an osprey catching fish. Either he feels lazy or eagles don't think it's bad to steal. Rather than fish for himself, at top speed he flies toward the osprey. Screaming loudly in a power dive, Heli seems ready to strike it with his talons. After several attacks from Heli the scared osprey drops the fish and flies to safety. Quickly Hali flips on his back, catches the fish in his talons, and carries it back to his nest.

By fall the young eagles have learned to hunt and kill food on their own. At night they still sleep in the nest with their parents. When ice begins to form on the lake, the eagles head south together.

Reaching their winter feeding grounds, the young eagles fly off on their own. Life becomes easier for the parent birds. Hali and Leuco roost in the trees at night, hunt in the morning, and often play air tag in the afternoon. Hali flies high with a stick. When he drops it, Leuco catches it in the air. Then she takes her turn. The two play the game for a long time. Then they hunt for their evening meal, which might be mice, squirrels, ducks, rabbits, or their favorite—fish.

When spring arrives Hali and Leuco return again to their nest by the lake.

Two days of hiking took them into the Klamath Mountains and the Siskiyous. One night they camped under a huge sugar pine. Scattered about the tree were dozens of mammoth cones. "Dad, let's play football with these huge cones. Look, this one must be 20 inches long."

Dropping out of Marble Mountain Wilderness, the trail wanders through rugged country for about 40 miles. It crosses the Klamath River near the village of Seiad Valley.

"Kenny, I've got sad news for you. The next village is the last trailside settlement in California. And that means the end of our journey for this year."

"I feared you'd be saying that soon, Dad."

"We'll call Mother at the tiny store/post office. This little town of about 100 people is at the most northern tip of California, not far from Interstate 5. We can wait there until she can come and get us."

"So this is our last hike before school begins. But we'll have all winter to study the guidebook and plan to see Oregon and Washington next year," Kenny said. "I'll enjoy that part of geography class."

"You'll have lots to tell Mom when she gets here," Dad said with a smile. "What a great summer we've had!"

"Except it went too fast. I'm glad we can hit the Crest Trail next year. But Dad, something really bothers me about bald eagles."

"What's that?"

"You said they have no natural enemies, except human beings. The past few weeks we've noticed that people had taken much of the land for crops and lumber. Do farmers still shoot the eagles when they lose a chicken? Do collectors still steal eagle eggs and sell them? Why are people trying to get rid of their national bird?"

"Cheer up, Kenny. There's hope for the bald eagle. A law has been passed to protect the bird. I'm sure that in the years to come you'll still see a pair of eagles soaring, circling, up and up until they become specks against the blue."

"And when I see them, I'll think about when Jesus comes, and I, too, will be able to fly toward heaven." Kenny looked to the sky.

"Did you know Jesus gave you a promise for that?" Dad quoted from Isaiah, "'Those who wait on the Lord shall renew their strength. They shall mount up with wings like eagles. They shall run and not be weary. They shall walk and not faint'" (Isa. 40:31).

"What fun to fly side by side with an eagle! I can hardly wait!"

Dad gave Kenny a special smile.

6

North to Hinds and Stags

The Crest Trail in southern Oregon began at high altitudes through thick forests. Unfortunately, ugly logging roads abound. Then it drops to one of the lowest, driest, and least scenic sections found in either Washington or Oregon.

"Can't say that I appreciate all the eyesores left by loggers and the lack of wilderness sensation," Dad observed.

"But the lack of drinking water is worse. And we have more than 50 miles of this before we reach Fish Lake," Kenny complained.

"Cheer up, Kenny, after that we'll be hiking in Sky Lakes Wilderness. The guidebook says that area of the Cascades rivals in beauty any along the Pacific Crest Trail."

When they reached the Sky Lakes area, it rained some each day. Everywhere along the trail they skirted lots of little lakelets with streams connecting them. All this water brought out a tremendous mosquito population.

"I'd hate to get caught here without a tent. I'm glad ours has a screened door and window. Repellent doesn't seem to stop these eager little beasties," Kenny said as he swatted another one.

In spite of the mosquitoes, they marveled at the natural beauty both along the trail and the distant mountains.

But after 40 miles with the pesky insects, they longed for a change.

Kenny leaned against a tree and took a long drink from his canteen. "Wow, it's hot! I think southern Oregon plans to cook us."

"We'll have lots of days like this before we cover the 500 miles of Oregon this summer. But at the top of this dusty climb, you'll stand at the cool rim of Crater Lake."

An hour later Kenny exclaimed, "Wow! It's pretty! I've never seen such blue water."

"You're looking into a volcano. This one blew its top," Dad explained. "The lake looks deep blue because the steep cliffs around the lake go down 2,000 feet. After the volcano blew, it raised a cone in the center called Wizard Island."

"Almost looks like a castle. You know, Dad, I like the Cascade Range as much as the Sierra Nevada Mountains of California."

"The Pacific Crest Trail takes us near most of the main peaks of the Cascades—magnificent mountains like the Three Sisters, Washington, Jefferson, and Mt. Hood. My guess is we'll see lots of animals too. "

Hard wind and pelting rain struck the day they reached the Three Sisters. Heavy clouds hid the glaciers on the peaks. Pine needles drifted in pools of water as the two hikers set up their tent in a clearing near the trail.

Kenny sat looking out the tent door and watched the raindrops splatter on the leaves of the bushes. Dad lay on his sleeping bag while he read.

Suddenly Kenny grabbed Dad's leg. "Look! I see a big animal moving through the underbrush."

Dad sat up quickly. Moments later a female elk and her

calf stepped into the clearing. "There'll be more. They travel in herds," Dad whispered.

Five more hinds (sometimes called cows) with their calves followed. Busy eating grass, they paid no attention to the large male elk that joined them.

"What a rack of antlers he has!" Kenny felt goose pimples all over him. Peeking out their tent door, they watched the elk for 15 minutes until the herd slipped back into the forest. Unable to hold his excitement any longer, Kenny exclaimed, "Dad, I have oodles of questions to ask you about elk!"

"What makes you think I know all the answers?"

Tom, the Stag Elk

All summer Tom, a young stag (often called a bull), has stayed alone in the high ridges of the mountains while he grows new antlers. Still soft, they are covered with a growth called "velvet." Longer and thicker than the year before, the antlers have six points on each side. A handsome elk of two years, he has not yet joined the herd.

During the summer the hinds live apart from the stags, staying in the high valleys and hiding their newborn calves in the brush. As they guard them from coyotes and mountain lions, the mothers eat their fill, laying up fat and strength for the coming winter. While the hinds feed, the spotted babies lie down and stay put. Since the calves give off no smell, they are quite safe from enemies if they don't move.

By fall Tom's antlers have hardened into bone. He's shed the velvet by rubbing them on branches and small trees. Now he feels ready to show off his headgear during the coming mating season. The leaves on the maples have turned red and the aspens golden. Tom hears a sound that lures him from the high country. He hurries through the timber, eager to fight with the stag he heard bugling.

What a sound that bugle is! It will send chills up and down your spine no matter how many times you hear it. Stags use the bugle sound like they do their antlers. They like to challenge other males and take over the females in the herd.

When Tom sees the big elk, he has his head lifted high while he bugles. Tom now lowers his head, snorting and charging. Surprised, the more mature stag falls back a few steps. But he has more experience and strength than Tom. With a mighty lunge he knocks Tom to his knees. Before Tom can get to his feet and charge again, the old

stag lunges at him again. His added weight
and strength are no match for the young
Tom, who falls down again. He gains his
footing as the older male draws back for a
fresh charge. Tom knows he'd better turn
and run before he receives a bloody gash
in his side from those antlers. The old stag
chases Tom to the timber, then stops and
bugles his victory.

Young Tom has learned a lesson. He
needs more strength and power before he
can take over a herd. He hasn't grown up
yet. His bugle still sounds like a squeal. He
hears another voice like his own, and runs
toward it. In the moonlight he sees a young
stag his size.

The two young males snort and glare at
each other. Both charge at the same time.
They meet with a clash of antlers. For an
hour they charge and clash like two boys
in a wrestling match. One or the other is
driven to his knees only to spring back and
lunge again. They grow tired and rest before
beginning again.

At last Tom drives hard, steps back, and
lunges at the shoulder of the other male.
The pain from Tom's sharp antlers causes
the stag to totter. Before Tom can charge
again, the other animal gives up and runs
away. Tom, who chases him a short distance, has won his first battle. Feeling good,
he returns to the meadow and squeals out
a somewhat better sounding bugle.

The deep snows of December drive the

elk herds to the heavy grass that grows in the valley. Tom joins a band of elk with hinds, calves, and young stags like himself, plus the lead stag, who had won all the battles. But the real leader of the herd is a wise old hind. She guides the herd from place to place. Using her keen nose and sharp ears, she often stops to listen and sniff. One night she hears wolves howling in the distance.

Leaving the shelter of the trees, she takes the herd to the safety of open ground. The hinds and stags gather around the calves like spokes in a wheel. They wait, ready to defend themselves with their sharp hoofs and antlers. The wolf pack circles again and again.

Finally a large wolf lunges toward a female elk. At the same moment the old lead stag charges, catching the wolf with his antlers. Howling, the wolf lands in a heap, and a hind tramples him to death. Waiting wolves spring at her throat and the tendons on her rear legs. When she falls, half the pack plunges in for the kill. Tom and the other young stags stomp and slash at the wolves. While they fight, the other half of the pack attacks two calves. The old stag turns on them. Four wolves, still unhurt, turn and trot away. Another wolf, limping on three legs and with blood dripping from its wounds, follows them. None of the rest of the pack will ever fight again.

The elk have won. Yet they have lost several animals. By dawn the herd, limping and

bloody from the battle, follow the lead hind back toward the timber. Two females bawl loudly as they leave their dead calves lying in the snow. When the elk have gone, the few remaining wolves return to eat what they had killed.

Another year passes. By October Tom wears a perfect rack of antlers, and his bugle has full, rounded notes. No more squeal. Soon all the young stags that challenge him have given up and have run into the forest. Confident of his strength, he wants leadership. One by one, he defeats even the older males.

Then comes a moonlit night when he hears the bugle of a strange stag. In ringing notes Tom bugles his warning and runs to meet the challenge. The two big elk stand ready for a fight. They meet with a terrific crash, which sounds like a pine tree falling. Antlers tangle together. They struggle until they stand free again.

Both elk back up and charge again. On the far side of the meadow a herd of hinds and calves wait, eating as though nothing is happening. The crash of antlers drives the strange elk to his knees, but he's up again, ready for the next charge. The two huge elk snort and paw. Tom charges again, and their antlers lock. Pushing, shoving, they use all their strength. Twisting their heads pack and forth, they finally break away. Again Tom charges. The points of his antlers rip open the shoulder of the other male. Blood gushes out. They charge again. Back and forth they struggle. Both become very tired. They pause for rest. The other stag looks toward the females.

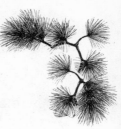

At that moment Tom charges and knocks the big elk to his knees. Struggling from loss of blood, he slowly staggers to his feet. With the little strength he still has, he flees to the safety of the trees. Tom watches him go. Then he raises his head in a bugle of victory. Walking over to the herd, he nudges several females. They now belong to him. Tom has become the lead stag.

Continuing northward, the two hikers followed the Crest Trail past Oregon's magnificent Mt. Washington and Jefferson Wilderness areas. Several times they came upon herds of elk.

"It's hard to believe these animals once lived across most of North America," Dad said as he sat down on a log. "Let's watch them feed while we rest. They don't seem to mind us if we keep our distance."

"Dad, I'm beginning to think that the elk's worst enemies aren't wolves and mountain lions, but greedy people who steal their mountains."

"You're right," Dad agreed. "Lumbering destroys the

forests. Thousands of grazing sheep ruin the elk's grass from the low valleys to the high country. Mining, roads, houses, and resorts drive the elk from their feeding grounds. Elk ranges have gotten smaller and smaller until now they're pushed into the high western mountains."

"No wonder the herds keep decreasing. Lots are killed during hunting season, too," added Kenny. "With their valleys gone and so little of the mountains left for them, where can they feed when the heavy winter snows come?"

Dad got up and started on. They hiked through a ghost forest of burned lodgepole snags and past abandoned logging roads. Kenny, thinking hard, followed him in silence. Finally Dad spoke. "I guess the only answer to your question is found in God's promise that will come true when He creates a new earth: 'They shall not hurt nor destroy in all my holy mountain'" (Isa. 65:25).

"Won't it be great when greed and selfishness are gone forever? I like to imagine a world where we'll all live together in peace!" Dad said. "But for now, give me the Crest Trail, the high country, and the wild animals and birds!"

Their route continued northward through a hemlock forest occupied by clicking Oregon juncos and drilling red-shafted flickers. After a brief ascent, they arrived at a long cliff-like ridge where Mt. Jefferson, 10,497 feet, towered above them in all its presidential glory. At the base of its south slope lay a weird volcanic landscape. "Looks spooky with all those spires. What's it called, Dad?"

"That's Cathedral Rocks. Judging by their color, they must have been formed in the Dark Ages," Dad said.

Each bend in the trail brought changing views. Spirea and rhododendron bordered the trail, interspersed with gooseberry, huckleberry, and corn lily's huge leaves. The sound of rushing water told them they were nearing a creek.

"I've been looking for Russell Creek," Dad said. "Glad

we've arrived here in the coolness of the morning. The guidebook warned us to cross before 11 a.m. The afternoon's warmer temperatures greatly increase the snowmelt from the glaciers. The fast, cold flow has swept some hikers down the gorge below this ford. The crossing may be a wet one, but it's still safe."

That night they camped at Scout Lake beneath the hemlocks on the north shore.

With camera in hand, Dad exclaimed, "What a perfectly framed view of Mt. Jefferson reflected on the lake! There it stands, stately, majestic, and beautiful with its white robe of glaciers."

"No wonder Jefferson Park is popular. Wish we could stay and enjoy these magnificent mountains, but tomorrow we head for Mt. Hood."

The way led through shady forests. Douglas fir and hemlocks. Red cedar. Silver, grand, and subalpine firs. Plus western white pine and lodgepole pine. The grandeur of these stately trees filled them with a feeling of awe. As he listened to the wind in the pines, Kenny had no trouble imagining the sound of angel's wings.

A few days later Kenny and his Dad picked up another package at Timberline Lodge, a large hotel built at 6,000 feet on the side of Mount Hood. They called Mom and made an appointment to meet her at the Columbia River Gorge. Glad to leave the tourists, they began their last hike in Oregon. For more than 50 miles they went in and out of steep-walled canyons. The trail, beautiful and dramatic, abounds in waterfalls as it descends into the spectacular Columbia River gorge. At Zigzag Canyon they camped near the cool spray of a 75-foot waterfall.

"Wow, what flowers!" Kenny sat surrounded by brilliant red paintbrush, lavender lupine, and many small flowers of yellow and white. "Makes me think of heaven with all this loveliness."

At Indian Mountain several days later, they stopped to eat and rest on a soft cushion of pink mountain heather. In the distance they saw the Columbia River Gorge.

"When we cross into Washington at the Bridge of the Gods, we'll be at the lowest elevation of the entire trail, only 155 feet above sea level," Dad said. "I'm glad Mom said she and Heather would meet us there. We can spend a few days in a motel before we start the challenges of Washington. We'll need some time to buy food and plan more "care" drops. You see, Kenny, after we leave the Columbia River, we must hike 125 miles before we can pick up another package. And during that time we'll climb to 7,080 feet elevation in alpine conditions. Now that's getting up there!"

"I keep telling myself, Dad, that we can make it a step at a time just as Grandma said down there at the Mexican border. And Jesus has surely given us the strength to keep going when we felt like dropping on the trail."

Finally they could see the highway and a parking lot. Kenny spotted two people looking upward with binoculars. With a yell he started to run toward a familiar-looking parked car.

"Mom, we're here!" And in moments he felt her arms holding him close.

7

Did That Get Your Goat?

The family spent several very busy but happy days together at a nearby motel. Mom had brought all kinds of goodies for them to enjoy. Fresh fruit never tasted better. Apples, oranges, peaches, grapes—Kenny couldn't get enough.

With a banana in one hand and a date bar in the other, Kenny exclaimed, "You brought five kinds of cookies, a pecan pie, and blueberry muffins, plus your wonderful whole wheat bread and raspberry jam! Sure wish we could take these on the trail."

Mother's eyes twinkled. "Both you and Dad have lost weight. Heather· and I had fun baking these treats, but it's more fun to watch you eat. Seems like we'll never fill you up. Hope there's some left to fill your pockets when your start out again. How many more miles do you have until you reach Canada?"

"We have about 480 miles to hike in Washington. This is divided into five sections. The first takes us to White Pass, near Mt. Rainier. The second to Interstate 90, at Snoqualmie Pass. Then we go to Highway 2, at Stevens Pass; on to Highway 20, at Rainy Pass; and finish at Manning Provincial Park in British Columbia, Canada. Most of this covers rugged mountains and deep canyons. I've marked each place where we'll need to have food packages sent. As soon as we get them packed and addressed, we can be on our way again," Dad answered.

That night they all studied the map. Dad pointed out special features. "Tomorrow we leave the lush, damp Columbia River forest to climb viewless dry slopes and rocky bluffs toward Blue Lake. It's some 20 miles away, the next place with good water."

"And Mom, would you like to know where the mosquitoes are thick, the water's scarce, and we'll get into heavy snow patches?" Kenny asked.

"Sure would. You sound like an experienced backpacker." Mother smiled approvingly.

Early the next morning they parted. "Thanks so much for meeting us here, Mom. If it weren't for you, we'd never make it. Takes a lot of determination to keep going some days. But we know you're praying for us. And we'll be looking forward to seeing you at Manning Park by September 15, we hope."

Kenny and Dad hugged her again, watched her drive away, and then started north from the Bridge of the Gods toll road. The trail wound through Douglas fir and maple trees that provided plenty of shade. It helped a lot, because the bright sun made the day feel hot.

"Thirty trail miles north of the Columbia River, we'll enter Indian Heaven. For centuries the Yakima Indians, who now live on the nearby Yakima Indian Reservation, came here in the autumn to harvest wild huckleberries," Dad said the next day. "We're now entering the Gifford Pinchot National Forest!"

They came upon a rolling meadowed expanse of huckleberry patches and tiny lakes.

"Do the Indians still come here?" asked Kenny.

"Yes, about 800 acres of national forest land is reserved for their use. When the dark blue huckleberries hang heavy on the bushes, the Yakima Indians from the reservation east of here all come and enjoy this place. They put up their tepees and harvest the berries. They also sell many of them at roadside stands."

The trail provided excellent views of Mount St. Helens (9,677 feet) like a pyramid of snow to the northwest, and the blue-grey rocky wall of Mount Adams (12,307 feet) to the northeast. Across the Columbia to the south they could still see the white cap of Mt. Hood (11,235 feet) peaking above the horizon. In the distance rose the misty white of Mt. Rainier to the north. Both hikers, tired and thirsty, welcomed the sight of the clear waters of Blue Lake nestled at the foot of Gifford Peak.

"Let's camp here tonight," Kenny suggested.

The next day the trail became increasingly steep as they headed for Mt. Adams Wilderness. Many switchbacks brought them closer to the mountain. The trail stays just above timberline. They continued to Killen Creek, which flows over a sloping stone cliff. This creates a 40-foot cascade of white water on black rock.

"What a delightful contrast," Dad commented as he took another picture.

At the bottom, the churning waters soon quieted and flowed across a meadow. Again and again Kenny and his dad came upon fresh views of the mountains. Each time they stopped to admire.

"Wow, what a view! Mt. Adams with its glaciers, and majestic Rainier, the highest mountain in Washington." Dad stretched his arm in a half circle.

"Don't ignore Mount St. Helens, the volcano that blew off 1,000 feet from its peak. When did you say that happened, Dad?"

"In 1980."

Kenny added. "I can still see the tip of Mt. Hood to the south. Dad, I feel like we're on top of the world!"

Soon after they left Mt. Adams wilderness, the terrain made them feel like they were hiking on the surface of the moon. Climbing to the summit of a high, bald hill they stopped in wonder. Before them lay the panorama of Goat Rocks Wilderness. The uneven ground littered with sharp rocks stretched as far as they could see along a ridge of crumbly volcanic rock streaked by snow and glaciers. All trees had vanished. None grew above timberline. Chilled by the strong cold wind, they pulled their windbreakers from their packs and donned them.

"Look at those dark clouds coming in! We could be in rain, sleet, or snow at this altitude in a few minutes. Since it's late afternoon, let's hunt for a sheltered campsite," Dad suggested.

"Good idea. Doesn't the weather man know it isn't supposed to snow in August? I know I'd endure the storm much better from the shelter of our tent," Kenny agreed.

They found a level place beneath the protection of a large rock out of the wind. Here they pitched their tent. Soon they could hear particles of ice landing on the canvas roof. They watched the sleet thicken and then change into snow. Then silence! In no time the ground all around them had turned white. Knocking the snow from the sagging roof, both Kenny and Dad crawled into their warm sleeping bags and were soon asleep.

After a damp, windy night, the hikers awoke to a clearing sky. They prepared for the 1,400 climb along the treeless ridge of the crest line of the Cascades. They walked along a rugged rocky trail over the the Goat Rocks. Cold mist danced about Goat Rocks wilderness.

74

"This is sure a bleak, windswept land. These crumbling volcanic rocks tell a story that long ago some mountain blew its top." Kenny stopped and knelt down. "Look Dad! This little evergreen tree is only six inches tall."

"It's called a juniper. Says something about the severity of this environment. We're in the realm of rock and ice." Dad pointed far below. "Down there, nestled below Johnson Peak, is Goat Lake. It's always frozen."

Near the top of Old Snowy Mountain, they attained the Pacific Crest Trail's highest point in Washington—7,620 feet. Ahead they could see the trail snaking into the swirling mist. For two miles they followed the sharp ridge. On either side the rocks dropped off into a foggy nothingness.

"This is spooky and scary too. Straight down on either side. Wonder how far it is? Sometimes the wind gusts are so strong I'm afraid I'll lose my balance," Kenny shouted above the wind.

Dad stopped and waited for him. He heard a movement near his feet. "Of all things, look who lives up here." Several ground squirrels and chipmunks played among the rocks. As they watched the small rodents, a sparrow hawk dived past them.

"Never thought birds and animals would live here, but they look fat and content," Kenny said. "Guess it's what you get used to."

When they approached Elk Pass the wind stopped, the mist cleared, and they saw the sun. On the horizon Packwood Lake shimmered as the rays of the sun reflected on the water. They stood motionless with awe at the sudden change.

"Look, Dad, I see something traveling across those steep cliffs." Kenny wriggled out of his pack and rummaged for his binoculars. "Wow, just look at what they can do! There's a whole bunch of mountain goats! One just leaped into space and landed on a small ledge. How do they live in this high country?"

Jumping Jack, the Mountain Goat

Across the top of the tall mountains of the world lies a cruel land where humans cannot live. The cold, strong winds make dwarfs of trees. Ice covers grass and flowers almost as soon as they grow. Terrible avalanches of snow, ice, and rocks rush down the steep slopes, destroying everything in their path. This is the land above timberline. Beautiful, but dangerous! Here Jumping Jack, a mountain goat, has learned to live despite great hardships.

Usually goat families live in small herds or bands. Most herds have a nanny, the mother goat, with her kid, the baby, a 2-year-old, plus 1- or 2-year-old goats called yearlings. Only at mating time are they joined by the billies or males, who spend their time alone or with other males.

Both male and female mountain goats look alike, with long, shaggy white hair. Each has sharp pointed horns, which can grow up to 8-11 inches.

One day late in May, Nanny Ruth leaves the rest of the herd in the upper valley. She finds a rock ledge, wider than most of those around her. It has an overhang of stone that offers some shelter if the weather turns bad. Standing alone on the ledge, she looks uncomfortable. Every few moments she hunches her back up and down. A baby goat is kicking within her. She feeds a little and lies down to sleep. Shortly before dawn the next morning, a tiny goat weighing about seven pounds is born.

As the nanny licks his wet fur, he straightens his wobbly legs. He falls twice before he gets under his mother. Reaching up with his tiny head, he finds one of her teats. Then he butts up against it to make the milk flow faster. The kid's tail stands erect as he sucks for about three minutes. His little legs seem made of rubber, because he drops to the ground, resting at his mother's feet. But not for long.

Before the kid is an hour old, he manages to climb over his resting mother. Then, seeing a medium-sized rock, he climbs to the top. Without fear he jumps down and lands on his nose. He lies beside her for a quick nap. As soon as he wakes up, he climbs the rock again, jumps and ends in another crash

landing. After he's nursed for a few minutes, he begins to whirl in circles. His nanny stands by the edge, watching him hop about, dance on his hind legs, and bleat so loudly that he can be heard across the valley.

All the while his mother keeps him on the uphill side. When he loses his balance, he falls against her legs instead of over the mountain's edge and off into space. When he sleeps, she makes sure he's on the summit side of her thick white coat, rather than the valley side.

On the second day the baby climbs more, leaps higher, and falls harder, though not as often. Little Jumping Jack earns his name, for he seldom walks. Instead he jumps, runs, slides, pushes, butts, and spins in circles. By his fourth day he has learned to bite off the blossoms of wild flowers. He likes glacier lilies, yellow bells, and spring beauties best. By day five he can keep up with his mother over rough ground, and has begun to chew his cud like all goats do.

That's when he meets another creature who lives above timberline, the golden-mantled ground squirrel. Jumping Jack pops straight up in the air, bleating a scared "Baa!" Taking shelter underneath his mother, he peeks out between her shaggy white legs. When she stomps her feet twice, the squirrel disappears. Since the kid no longer feels afraid, he begins to nurse.

Later that same day he runs to hide

beneath his mother twice. Once when the jay-like Clark's nutcracker bird flies close and lands on a rock. The second time is when a shadow crosses him as an eagle, who could easily pick up such a small animal in his talons, flies overhead.

Now mother and son join the herd. The other goats look and look at this tiny white climber. By the time Jack is 4 weeks old, he eats grasses, herbs, sedges, conifer needles, and lichens that hang from evergreen trees or cling to the rocks. He can dig for bulbs and roots, and he breaks stalks of bear grass. Though he still tries to nurse from time to time, his nanny steps over him and walks away.

God made Jumping Jack's body just right for climbing. His short legs are poor for running, but perfect for jumping and balance. His two-toed hooves each have wraparound toenails that he can use to catch and hold to a crack or knob of rock. Each toe comes to a point, which is just right for digging in dirt or packed snow. Best of all, he has a rough pad or sole on the bottom of his hooves that sticks out a little past the nail. This keeps him from skidding.

The two toes can spread far apart, which keep him from slipping when he's going downhill. They provide enough friction so that he won't slide. Also rock, gravel, dirt, or snow can wedge into the crotch of the V between his toes and act as a brake.

With two toes on each of his four feet—

eight in all—he can go almost anywhere safely. No wonder mountain goats can climb so well and so fast! One goat climbed 1,500 feet in altitude in 20 minutes with little effort. An experienced hiker followed him on the same path. He took one and a half hours and was dead tired when he got there!

Right away Jumping Jack begins to run and play with the other kids. Once when he can't find any other playmates, he makes friends with a hoary marmot that is resting in the sun. Creeping close he touches its nose and they race to a salt lick. Mountain goats need these mineral salts. The dry food they must eat all winter lacks many of these important minerals, which they need to stay healthy.

Uphill or downhill, Jack bounds head-on over the rocks. He has learned to leap into the air, flip around, and land facing the opposite direction. Using both his hooves and stomach, he can slide down almost vertical slopes by crawling like a fly. Nanny Ruth has taught him how to leap safely from ledge to ledge.

For the first year of his life, Jack stays close to his mother. She helps him find food and a place to sleep. When other goats try to fight him, she protects him. By now his horns are three inches long.

The cold of winter comes early above timberline. Again the mountain goat has just the right clothes to keep warm. Underneath his thick hide, Jack has a layer of thick fat that acts like padding or insulation against the cold. Covering his hide is a long, plush double coat of white fur with many, many air pockets that keep the heat inside.

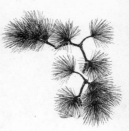

But don't his feet and toes get cold? Not any more than your hair or nails. Jack's hooves with the horny toenails and traction pads are tough, dry stuff that work just as well when the temperature is below zero as in the summer sun.

In early November when Jumping Jack is 6 months old, he notices that several older billy goats have come close to the herd. The billies act strange. They don't eat but just stand gazing at the nannies. This time of the year when the males get lovesick is called the rutting season. With each passing day the males come closer, but the nannies either run away or pay no attention to them. Still they keep following the nannies.

Little by little the nannies lose their fear, letting the billies come closer. Then just to prove they won't fight or hurt the nannies, the male goats act very humble. Jack watches one billy crawl toward his mother on his stomach and squeak tenderly like a baby goat. This wins her heart. She allows him to lick her and touch her. Soon after they mate, the billy leaves. If he hadn't, Nanny Ruth would have chased him away.

One winter day Jack and his mother are feeding on a windy ridge. Suddenly Nanny stops eating. Her ears go back and her tail up. Fear causes her humped back to shake

under her white fur. Jack knows something is wrong. Her black, beady eyes have seen a puff of dust rising, almost like smoke, the first signal of an avalanche.

In an instant she bounds up an ice wall with Jack at her heels. She knows every crack and cranny on that mountain wall. Jumping from ledge to ledge, mother and son run for their lives. The ground begins to shake. They can hear the rumble of the down-rushing mass of ice, snow, and rock as the mountainside falls into the valley below. Just as they reach solid rock, the awful mass roars past them. They feel the strong wind that the avalanche makes as it covers the trail they'd just left and flattens every tree in its way.

As the snowpack increases, grass and sedges are buried deep. Even Nanny's and Jack's sharp hooves can't break the ice. With food harder and harder to find, hunger faces them. As their bodies begin using the stored fat from the summer months, they become weak and thin. Now it's harder to fight off the cold winds and low temperatures.

Nanny decides she must leave the safety of the high rocks to hunt for food where the trees grow. Very few other wild animals bother the goats on their high ledges, but Nanny knows that Jack needs food soon or he'll starve. When they reach the evergreen trees, they eat the needles. But all the time Nanny's dark eyes watch. She knows that cougars and other enemies lurk in the forest, and goats cannot run fast on level ground.

Her sharp eyes see a small animal circling them. With each circle it comes in closer. Jack stays as close to Nanny as he can. Will this 30 pound animal with long curved claws and razor sharp teeth attack a goat that weighs nearly 200 pounds? The wolverine knows no fear. Before he can charge, Nanny lowers her sharp horns. Stomping and snorting, she lunges toward him. Jack hears the wolverine's growls and stays close behind Nanny. Though wolverines are fierce and seldom retreat in a fight, this one knows he'd be wise to turn and run from her dagger-like horns and sharp hooves. In moments he flees into the forest.

At least Nanny and Jack have no worry about grizzly bears, because all the bears are still asleep in their dens. Keeping a constant watch, Nanny stays in the trees, finding food for Jack until he seems stronger. When an early spring thaw melts some of the snow on the highlands, she gladly returns to the safety of the high rocks above timberline.

But it isn't entirely safe there, because with the warming temperatures, the avalanches increase. Snowslide after snowslide, like roaring locomotives, pass the herd of goats. One yearling doesn't jump soon enough and is carried down the mountain to his death.

Jack now weighs about 70 pounds. Though less than half the size of his mother, he is now a yearling and on his own,

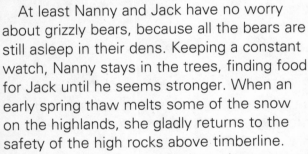

because Nanny Ruth left him when her new baby was born. How he misses her protection! Other goats in the herd often chase him. Some who are 2 years old, threaten him with their horns. These mock battles teach Jack important lessons. He learns how better to defend himself from enemies that might prey on him. He watches them find scarce food hidden in the cracks on steep cliffs.

Each day Jack gains more knowledge on how to survive at the top of the world where there's no place for comfort. He learns to know the mountains and can find the best trails that lead to safety. The older animals lead him to overhangs and crevices that offer shelter from a mountain blizzard. He huddles together with them in rain, sleet, or lightning. He finds shade from the burning sun of summer.

By the time Jumping Jack has become an adult goat of 3 years, he can sprint on the edges of cliffs and dash along sheer precipices in safety. He feels at home climbing huge boulders where other animals fear to go. Jack has learned how to live above timberline.

After a good night's rest, Kenny stepped out of his tent and gasped in wonder. Only 30 miles away, rising from a throne of low clouds, he saw "The Mountain," majestic, kingly Mount Rainier, protruding into the blue sky at 14,410 feet.

"Wow, what a mountain!"

Kenny said that over and over again as they enjoyed one view after another of snow-covered Mount Rainier along the trail to White Pass. Here they picked up several much needed "care" packages, washed their clothes at the place provided for hikers, and called home.

"We have 98 miles to Snoqualmie Pass and no supplies available en route. Glad we sent two packages ahead, as there isn't much to buy here," Dad said.

How they enjoyed the spectacular trail from White Pass to Chinook Pass! Again they marveled at the panorama—striking views of Mt. Rainier, Goat Rocks, Mt. Adams, and Mount St. Helens. North of Chinook Pass, the forest thinned, and the wildflowers thickened. By mid-August the pasque flowers that bloom on the edge of a snowbank had become silky tassels looking much like a rag mop head.

"That's why they call them 'the old man of the mountain'," Dad explained.

Deep creamy-white bear grass covered the meadows along the trail. "Elk and bear eat a lot of these. Bears particularly like the juicy base of the plants. So do small rodents."

Bright splashes of purple Rainier gentians, white bistort, lavender lupines, pearly everlasting, deep maroon Indian paintbrush, orange monkey flowers—the list is endless—lined the trail.

Dad stopped often to shoot many pictures of these alpine gardens planted by the hand of the Master Gardener. Rounding a bend in the trail, they came upon a herd of mountain goats.

"I really like those guys. Doesn't matter to them if they're on smooth boulders, jagged rocks, or glassy ice, they know their mountains. Look, they're going almost straight up." Kenny whistled in admiration as he watched them climb the steep rocks.

"Wouldn't life be great if we'd do as they do, meet our problems by clinging to Jesus, our Rock?"

Kenny grinned and rested against a big boulder. "I'm ready for another of your mini-sermons, Dad. How do I cling to that Rock?"

"Simple. Know and trust God's promises. They'll keep you just as safe as those goats on that ledge. But remember, if you do get to a dead-end road or on the wrong path, be as smart as the goats and don't go blindly on. Follow their example. Look up, turn around, and press close to the Rock, Jesus."

"Hey, that's neat, Dad! I'll remember what you said." And Kenny smiled at his father.

8

The End of the Trail

After picking up another food package at Snoqualmie Pass, the two hikers noted that they had 238 miles to the Canadian border.

"This could be the toughest hiking yet," Dad said as he studied the map. "We'll hike 71 miles from here to Stevens Pass through the Alpine Lakes Wilderness. If the weather is bad this could be a cold, windy miserable trek. In clear weather it's glorious with views of Mt. Rainier and Mt. Baker. You'll like this alpine country. Plenty of steep valley walls that will lead us down to rushing glacier-fed streams, but expect some cold crossings."

The next week seemed endless. Completely exhausted, Kenny panted, "Wish we had feet like mountain goats. First we trudge up the mountains, then straight down and then up again. There must be hundreds of steep switchbacks in and out of these deep canyons."

They slipped and slid in mud around ponds and lakes. But most of all Kenny dreaded fording the dangerous rivers. About halfway to Stevens Pass they came to Waptus Lake.

"How's this? Come, my weary hiker. Rest from your day's toil. Enjoy the scenic glory of this blue lake surrounded by towering mountains." Dad threw down his pack and flopped on the ground beside Kenny.

As they rested by the lake, Kenny looked around. "Looks like God had a great time here! Everywhere in mountain meadows and on the hillsides, I see bluebells, columbines, vanilla leaf, and lots of flowers I can't name. Looks like a carpet of blossoms under the fir, hemlock, pines, and cedar."

"Magnificent scenery!" Dad agreed. "What a garden He planted! Ferns fill in between the splashes of color with mountains, lakes, and streams as a backdrop. And the guidebook says there are 750 glaciers in this wilderness. Wonder how many we can see from here."

During the night Kenny awakened with a start. What was that strange sound? He listened. Whatever it was, it sounded close to the tent. He remembered seeing a bear on the far side of the lake just before sunset. He heard it again—like heavy breathing ending in a snort. Was it a bear? A cougar? He pulled his arm out of the sleeping bag and touched Dad.

"Wake up," he whispered, "and listen."

Dad turned over and grunted, "What'd you say?"

"Shhhh. There's something prowling around our tent. Be quiet and listen." Several minutes passed. Then they both heard it—louder and closer. Dad reached for his flashlight, but kicked his pack where the cooking utensils were. The noise he made scared away whatever was out there. The beam of the flashlight revealed nothing.

"Guess we'll never know who visited us," Dad said as he turned over and went back to sleep again.

The next night Kenny heard the same sound. He had an eerie feeling. Fear caused goose pimples all over his body. He'd placed his flashlight beside his head the night before. Quietly he sat up and beamed it through the screened window. Nothing. By this time Dad awakened.

"Still hunting for bears?"

"Can't find anything out there, but I know I heard it again."

"Let's say you're having a bad dream. Maybe those little mice we saw last evening can make another sound than the squeak we heard. For now I'm going back to sleep."

The mystery remained nature's secret.

Next day they began the arduous climb to Deception Pass. The trail from the pass to Deception Lake crosses a grassy plateau dotted with small pools and large boulders.

"Looks like a spacious Japanese rock garden," Dad said.

But Kenny found the abundant huckleberries much more interesting than glaciers. He gathered handfuls as he hiked, to stuff in his mouth as soon as it was empty. "Think I'll stop and pick some for dessert tonight and for our granola tomorrow morning. We could get a quart in no time." And they did.

"Sure great that Mother Nature is supplying us with all these berries. Helps supplement our dwindling supply of food. Should be arriving at Stevens Pass soon, where we'll pick up a couple more packages." Dad looked hopeful.

Late that afternoon they left Stevens Pass, glad for full packs of food again. "Let's hike to Lake Valhalla before we stop for supper. It's only about six miles. Maybe we can camp there." Dad started out through a bushy stretch past a floral assortment of asters, fireweed, bleeding heart, and white Sitka valerian.

They followed Stevens Creek through a narrow valley decked with the reds and golds of autumn. The sun was low when they arrived at the lake. Dropping their packs, they noticed a busy little animal biting off stalks of lupine and carrying them to his burrow.

"That's a pika or cony," Dad said. "He's a chubby little guy. Notice there is no visible tail. Very active in the day-time gathering small piles of fresh hay and placing them on the rocks to dry in the sun. He stores them deep in his burrow for the winter. If we're quiet, maybe we'll hear his peculiar short high-pitched squeaks. He's a sure sign cold weather is near."

As they ate they watched the pika rush to get all his hay stored away. "I like him—not a bit afraid of us. Hey, Dad, Look! God's going to give us another treat—the sunset colors reflected on the lake," Kenny said. "You going to take a picture of that?"

From pink, red, and orange, the colors deepened to burgundy and mauve. After a while a full moon climbed from behind the mountain.

"See how that shaft of light from the moon stretches the full length of the lake? Since it's too cold for mosquitoes, let's just spread our sleeping bags on a tarp and enjoy this peaceful place. Why have a roof over our heads and miss the beauty," Dad suggested.

"Great idea! I'll use my backpack for a pillow, and I'm all set for the night. Keep your flashlight ready, Dad. We just could have visitors here, too."

"Thank you, God, for giving us so much beauty," Dad prayed as they ended their evening worship. They wanted to stay awake and drink in the peace and joy of the moment, but both were too tired to keep their eyes open but a few minutes.

Sometime later Kenny became conscious of movement. Wide awake in an instant, he opened his eyes and saw close to his face a small deer licking the belt of his backpack. Kenny didn't move. Then he heard the little creature make a noise——the same sound he had heard the other nights. Kenny saw the little tongue reach out and lick again, obviously enjoying the salts from the sweat of Kenny's body from wearing the backpack.

Just then Dad moved and the startled creature leaped into the night.

"What a neat experience!" Kenny exclaimed. "We've solved the mystery! And I had the thrill of sharing a special moment with that beautiful animal."

The next morning Dad outlined the days ahead. "We're entering the rugged wonderland known as the North Cascades or America's Alps. For difficulty this section of the trail ranks second only to the High Sierras in California, which we had to skip because of the heavy snow. Winding around massive Glacier Peak we'll brake going down and labor going up the deep-floored canyons. The trail leads across many dangerous fords. In addition, this time of the year we could have threatening weather and persistent insects. We've got 116 miles to hike before we get to Rainy Pass. Are you willing to set out, or shall we go back and call Mom?"

"Never. With Jesus' help we can finish what we started. Let's be on the way."

As they ate their lunch that day, they saw half a dozen hoary marmots sunning themselves on a rock slide some distance away.

"Marmots are social animals," Dad explained. "They hibernate for almost nine months out of a year, because their rock slides are buried beneath deep snow. Notice that while the others are resting there's always one that acts as a sentinel or guard. When danger comes, he'll give his shrill whistle and all the marmots will disappear into the rock slide."

A few minutes after Dad spoke they heard a chorus of shrill whistles. Then they saw the reason. A large red-tailed hawk glided past above the rocks where they had been. A few minutes after he flew away, the marmots came out of their hiding places, one by one. At first they whistled softly, and then loudly as if declaring, "This is our home. Leave us alone!"

The next day they met many short-term hikers hurrying toward Stevens Pass. After about a dozen had passed them, Dad asked, "How come all you hikers are going one direction? What's the hurry?"

"Haven't you heard? There's a big storm coming. We've no desire to get caught out here in this wilderness at such high elevations. Could last for days."

As they hiked, they talked. "We're almost 18 miles from Stevens Pass and coming close to Pear Lake. Do you think we could tough out a storm, or shall we go back?" Dad asked.

"It will soon be September, and we're still a long way from Canada. We've got plenty of food and enough fuel for our stove. Let's ask Jesus to tell us what to do," Kenny suggested.

After prayer they decided to trudge on. Gray clouds covered the sky the next day, but the rain held off until late afternoon. With only a drizzle at first, they hiked until it poured.

"Too bad it didn't wait to rain until we got to Rainy Pass. Let's hunt for a shelter," Kenny suggested. "I'm glad we wrapped everything in plastic garbage bags this morning so that the things in our packs will stay dry even if our packs get wet." The strong wind pounded the rain against them. They were soaked to the skin.

Soon they saw a side trail. Following it a few yards, they found a natural cave formed by an overhanging cliff somewhat sheltered from the wind.

"This is just right," Dad commented as he set down his pack. "I'm sure we can start a fire here and dry out our boots and clothes. Though we'll get wet hunting wood, we can stay warm and keep dry, too. Just hope this storm doesn't continue for a week."

It rained without stopping all night. The wind blew so hard that they feared it might whip the tent off the ground. All the next day the heavy rain continued. They thanked God for the shelter. And then came the Sabbath.

"Didn't God plan a perfect place for us to spend His rest day?" Kenny said with a smile. "And I need another day off from hiking for my blisters to heal."

Finally the storm blew itself out. The two hikers were glad when they could step out into a soggy, wet world and see bits of blue between the clouds. "We're on our way, Dad!" Kenny shouted. Tired of being cooped up in a tent, he let out a whoop of delight.

During the next few days, they noticed on the mountain slopes more bushes and trees that had turned gold, orange, and red. Dwarf maples and larches now wore yellow, huckleberry bushes scarlet, and mountain ash trees orange. The bushes, still loaded with berries, were Kenny's constant delight. Yet as he picked, he always kept one eye open just in case a bear might be picking nearby. But the traveling was rough as they conquered one pass after another. Kenny counted them—Indian Pass, White Pass, Red Pass, Fire Creek Pass, and on. All were overshadowed by ice-clad Glacier Peak (10,568 feet). From Suiattle Pass, they followed a forested gorge to the Stehekin River. Here the boundaries of Glacier Peak Wilderness, North Cascades National Park, and Lake

Chelan National Recreation Area all met.

"Let's leave the trail and go to the nearby community of Stehekin on Lake Chelan. Not only will we pick up another food parcel, but we can check in at the lodge for the night and enjoy a shower, a hot meal, a good bed, and wash our clothes," Dad said.

"And call Mother," Kenny added. "She'll be glad we've weathered the storms."

That night at the lodge revived their courage and strength to continue. About 15 miles from Lake Chelan they reached Rainy Pass.

"Well, son, we've only 69 miles over eight passes till we reach Manning Provincial Park. But there's no more supply points either. Still I have good news for you. September is the best month to hike this stretch, because the mosquitoes are almost gone and the heavy snows don't usually start until October."

"May I look at the guidebook, Dad?" Kenny studied it for some time. "Just as I feared. Says, 'Beware of exceptions.' So we could face snow too. Listen to the names of the passes we must cross, Cutthroat, Methow, Glacier, Harts, Windy, Holman, Woody, and Hopkins."

They found it difficult to find good campsites with water nearby. At Harts Pass the weather turned cold and the rain began. Donning their rain jackets and pants, they kept on. Soon the rained turned to snow. Wearily they sloshed along the trail in a heavy snowstorm.

"I hope this doesn't get too deep. We didn't bring our snowshoes on this trek," Dad observed. "We should be at the Canadian border in about four days, that is if we can follow the trail in the snow."

With the compass, maps, and trail markings, they made slow progress. At Windy Pass they crossed into Pasayten Wilderness. That night they camped in a stand of pines at

Goat Lakes Basin. Sitting by the fire, they heard a sound like the stamping of boots.

When they heard it again, Dad suggested, "Let's walk toward the trees and see what's there." They heard the sound again, but could see nothing in the beam of the flashlight. So they returned to the fire, puzzled. Then the sound came again. Kenny turned and flashed the beam a few feet away. Two yellow eyes gleamed in the light, and they could see a graceful deer.

"Isn't she a beauty! Thanks for stopping by to visit a couple of weary hikers," Kenny called out into the night.

Finally the day came to make their last camp. They were at Hopkins Lake, just seven miles from the Canadian border. Because of the crisp, cold evening air, they put on their mitts and sat very close to their campfire.

"We made it one step at a time, son. Tomorrow is the end of our long journey," Dad said, looking into the glowing fire.

"And I loved every bit of it! All the wildflowers, animals, birds, rocks, clouds, thunderstorms, yes even the rain, snow, and hail."

"Plus the blisters on your feet, the sunburn on your nose, and the days when your legs were so tired you could hardly walk? How about the icy rivers we waded through?"

"That doesn't matter now, Dad. The joys are far better than the troubles. I can see in my mind the long trail that began at the barbed wire fence in the desert on the Mexican border. We have so many memories— starlit nights, sunsets reflected on lakes, marmots whistling, ground squirrels eating from our fingers, deer drinking by a stream, the cougar, and the bears who watched us from a distance. It's been great, Dad."

"What you've said reminds me of a special message Paul wrote in a letter to his friends in Corinth. Let me read it for you." Dad took out his Bible and read by firelight: "Therefore we do not lose heart. . . . For our light and momentary troubles are achieving for us an eternal glory that far outweighs them all. For we fix our eyes not on what is seen, but on what is unseen. For what is seen is temporary, but what is unseen is eternal." (2 Cor. 4:16-18, NIV).

"I like that, Dad. Our hike has been a lot like life's longer journey. God has led us all the way, over deep snow, through icy waters, and into peaceful flower-dotted meadows."

"And son, very soon we'll step with Him into the eternal. The beauties of the Pacific Crest Trail will seem as nothing compared to the joys He's prepared for us when He makes this world into the New Earth. Let's thank Him for being our Third Hiker."

And they prayed together in the firelight.